Nature's Pharmacy

C000098845

NATURE'S PHARMACY

A History of Plants and Healing

CHRISTINE STOCKWELL

Published in association with the Royal Botanic Gardens, Kew

ARROW BOOKS

For Lucy and Sally

Arrow Books Limited
62–65 Chandos Place, London WC2N 4NW

An imprint of Century Hutchinson Limited

London Melbourne Sydney Auckland
Johannesburg and agencies throughout
the world

First published by Century 1988

Arrow edition 1989

Text copyright © Christine Stockwell 1988
Drawings on pp. 40, 143, 149 copyright © Christine Stockwell 1988
All other illustrations copyright © Royal Botanic Gardens, Kew 1988

The illustration on p. 1 is of a nasturtium

This book is sold subject to the condition that it shall not, by way of trade or otherwise, be lent, resold, hired out, or otherwise circulated without the publisher's prior consent in any form of binding or cover other than that in which it is published and without a similar condition including this condition being imposed on the subsequent purchaser

Printed and bound in Great Britain by
The Guernsey Press Co. Limited
Guernsey, C.I.

ISBN 0 09 965760 0

Contents

Acknowledgements

This book comes from my being entrusted to reorganise the Pharmaceutical Society's Museum Collection of medicinal plants, after it had gone to the Royal Botanic Gardens at Kew, and from the suggestion made to me that some of the information attached to its contents could make interesting reading. Responsible for these two prompts were, respectively, Rosemary Angel, former head of the Museums Department and her successor, Dr Brinsley Burbidge. To them, Rupert Hastings, for his compiling the list of botanic names, David Field, for his proofreading and all members of the Gardens' staff who have helped, go my thanks. The illustrations were provided by the library at Kew Gardens and reproduced initially by the photographic department and I am grateful to those who assisted my seeking and selecting them.

I am particularly grateful to J. David Phillipson, Professor of Pharmacognosy at The School of Pharmacy, London University, for agreeing to read the first draft of the text, correcting blunders and making suggestions where necessary, and for providing a first vote of confidence in his kindly stated foreword. My thanks also go to John Ferguson, Secretary and Registrar of the Pharmaceutical Society of Great Britain, for his encouragement at the outset of the project and for the introduction to Professor Phillipson.

For editorial and typing help in the preparation of the manuscript I am much indebted to Nikki Aduba and, once it was with the publishers, to Valerie Buckingham for her patience and help in its completion.

Foreword

The inspiration for this book came during the time that Christine Stockwell was helping to catalogue and rehouse the collection of crude drugs and herbaria of the Pharmaceutical Society of Great Britain in its new abode at the Royal Botanic Gardens at Kew. Although commitment to the book came at a later stage, there is no doubt that some of the magic of the collection rubbed off on to the author. An affection for plant medicines and the wonders of the discoveries of such drugs as morphine and codeine from the opium poppy, quinine from the bark of the *Cinchona* tree and digoxin from the foxglove, is obvious in the pages of *Nature's Pharmacy*.

What is this collection which has held such sway over the author? It is a collection of natural substances used throughout the world as medicines. The collection was built up at The Pharmaceutical Society under the curatorship of a series of world experts including Theophilus Redwood, E. M. Holmes and T. E. Wallis. During the past thirty to forty years the majority of medicines dispensed in Great Britain has been in the form of tablets or capsules containing a single, mainly synthetic, powerful medicinal substance. The plant medicines which were familiar to previous generations no longer had medical approval and consequently it was believed that plant drugs were no longer of any importance. It was during this period that The Pharmaceutical Society changed the location of its headquarters and the collection was first transferred to the Department of Pharmacy, University of Bradford where it remained under the care of Professor J. M. Rowson and Dr W. E. Court until 1983, when a new home was made available at Kew.

7

Kew is a fitting resting place for such an historical collection and certainly there is an appreciation there of the contribution which plants have made to medicine. The question arises in this book as to whether there is any future in plant medicines or will they be relegated to those parts of world development which now include the dinosaur and the dodo.

It is perhaps not realised that although plant parts or green extracts no longer form part of our prescriptions in the UK, isolated constituents do form a considerable proportion. In the USA, it is known that 25 per cent of all prescriptions dispensed in community pharmacies (that is, chemists' shops) contain an active ingredient which owes its origin to a plant product. A knowledge of the chemistry of plant drugs has enabled synthetic analogues to be prepared and many painkillers are based on the structure of morphine, whilst muscle relaxants have been synthesised using the structure of tubocurarine, the active principle of the South American arrow poison, curare, as a template. A wider view of the world reveals that 80 to 90 per cent of the population cannot afford the products of the Western pharmaceutical industry and rely on their traditional, mainly plant, medicines.

Hence it is my belief that the past of plant medicines is only just the beginning and it takes a non-medical, non-scientific writer such as Christine Stockwell to point out what should be obvious to the experts. Read this book, enjoy it – I certainly did!

J. David Phillipson
Professor of Pharmacognosy
The School of Pharmacy
University of London
29–39 Brunswick Square
London, WC1N 1AX

1

Complaints and Cures

The saying goes that God created no complaint for which He did not also provide a cure, reflecting Him in a more benevolent mood, but there was a time when it was believed, as it is by some groups still, that when the disobedience of man aroused His wrath disease was the punishment, and the Almighty alone had the right to alleviate it.

In the first instance, whether we believe that a creator or natural selection was responsible for the way things came to be, it is true to say that most diseases can be avoided or cured with the right knowledge. Secondly, whether they are still termed human vices, or sympathetically reduced to foibles by the term 'human weaknesses', our over-indulgences are often the cause of disease; in fact, a self-inflicted punishment.

'A little of what you fancy does you good' is fine so long as it is not taken as a licence to every excess. But it is in what we fancy that we are most likely to want to over-indulge. Factors essential to the survival of our species have to make us feel good, otherwise we would not bother with them and the human race would peter out. If eating were not a pleasant experience, few would remain well nourished. If the sexual act were unpleasant, the species would have little chance of perpetuating itself. The sensations that activity stimulates have to be preferable to the feeling of inertia, otherwise we would all sit around and wait for the end to come. Similarly, the comfort of relaxed well-being is an obviously more beneficial state than one of irritability and tension. Natural selection has geared us to enjoy the things that will ensure our survival, but it has not provided us with an automatic means of putting on the brakes in time. In the West, we tend to eat too much, drink too much and have provided ourselves with the means of enjoying sexual freedom without having to bear the responsibilities and consequences of procreation.

The instinct to maintain a balance with the environment and within our own bodies does not seem to have evolved with our species as it has with others. Perhaps it has been lost or forgotten, but though we are still able to recognise warning signals, they are generally ignored and it is usually the doctor who has to point out, in the end, that it is time to call a halt.

It can be argued that each individual has the right to choose his own route to the devil, and decide the condition in which to maintain his body. But not everyone does have that choice, and deprivation is the other side of the coin.

Raspberry
Rubus idaeus
A tea made from the leaves was a popular remedy for diarrhoea and was also used to prevent miscarriages

There may be natural causes, such as famine, flood or fire (still officially termed Acts of God) but, more often than not, deprivation is a condition inflicted by one society on another, through aggression or indifference, which the victims, as in poverty or war, are seldom in a position to alter. Deprivation, whether of knowledge, caring, medicines or the money to pay for these, is preventable and the diseases it brings are curable. But it is not always in the best personal interests of the more fortunate to share what they have with those that have less. Worse still, many would not only be disinclined to offer support, but they may well deliberately withdraw it and, until universal well–being becomes a matter of universal concern, the historic imbalance will remain between those that have plenty and those that have nothing.

Of course, disease can be inherited, or can occur in the best looked–after body, but the folk principle that it is a result of either too little or too much of something still applies in the majority of cases. To begin to rectify these imbalances, personally or socially, some knowledge of the factors involved is needed.

Medical ignorance is not bliss but there has long been a suspicion that those within the profession prefer, and even plot, to keep their patients in it. Happily, this suspicion is generally unfounded, and most doctors would agree that a patient's intelligent understanding of his complaint makes doctoring an easier task. They would also agree, however, that ignorance is preferable to half truths. But where is the patient or curious lay person to go if he or she wishes to reach a general understanding of the relationship between complaint and cure?

The role of patient is one that, unfortunately, most of us have played at some time during our lives, and we each deliver our lines after our own instinctive fashion – tragically, melodramatically, with feeling, with pathos – but to most of us, unless we also happen to be part of the medical profession, it is an amateur role. Sometimes the term 'professional patient' is deservedly applied by the cynical doctor, but it is no commendation. We may be good patients, untroublesome ones, but medical amateurs most of us remain. We take what is prescribed by the doctor and prepared by the pharmacist in the hope that we will feel a good deal better than we did before. No questions asked.

Usually our condition is explained in simple terms and, before the ink has dried on the flimsy page from the prescription pad, we are outside the surgery door, kicking ourselves for not having queried such and such. If we do ask questions, and are lucky enough to have a doctor who is prepared to go through our case point by point with us, the ailment itself is usually more easily understood than its treatment, although even here communication can flounder due to differing terminology used by doctor and patient. A case of medical terms versus waiting room jargon. We suffer 'troubles' and 'problems'; the doctor hears and diagnoses complaints and symptoms. We may suffer heart trouble, back trouble or skin trouble. We may have chest or breathing problems, or hormonal problems. We may suffer from nerves, have some sort of infection, or that grand old euphemism, an upset tummy. To the doctor, these are complaints of the cardiovascular system, musculo-skeletal disorders, skin complaints, malfunctions of the respiratory system, the hormones, the central nervous system or the gastrointestinal tract.

Treatment is even more variable. If it happens to involve surgery, which can be more graphically explained and understood, it is easier for the patient to see the relationship between cure and complaint; in fact many are able to give a pretty good rendering of their 'ops' for the benefit of their friends and brethren of the waiting room. The real breakdown in communication comes with the medicines we take.

In this general confusion we cannot be blamed for finding alternative treatments somehow more attractive, yet those that practise them are often to blame for unnecessary scaremongering among their converts, which only helps to perpetuate half truths, does no good to itself or orthodox medicine and still less to the patients. It should be the aim of both alternative and orthodox practitioners to reconcile their approaches, not to segregate them. It is sad that taking a stand should be more important than taking the time for discussion in such a vital matter as good health, but it is the way of those with opposing views to war first and make peace treaties later. Meanwhile, the patient plays pig in the middle, and believes what he wants to hear from the side offering the most sympathy. To some alternative practitioners, not necessarily guaranteed an income from their profession, it is a sensible financial tactic to be more sympathetic or, if they are unethical, to belittle the medicines of their rivals.

Exponents of the advantages of health foods are right to say that refined food is less beneficial than whole food, when refined means reduced. White flour, for instance, is reduced to this form by removing the better part of the grain. The same argument does not always hold true for natural medicines. It may be that in

12

Camomile
Chamaemelum nobile
A tea made from the flowers is beneficial in cases of colic and stomach
cramps

some cases natural sources do provide chemical compounds that act in accord with one another in ways that cannot be predicted or synthesised. In this case they are used in the manufacture of orthodox medicines, but even these are seldom acknowledged by the exponents of 'natural cures'. It has become almost fashionable to talk knowingly (though seldom informedly) about the dangers of 'side effects' and, since these became popular propaganda against the drugs manufactured by the pharmaceutical industry, many dissatisfied patients claim to have experienced them in varying degrees of seriousness, and believe that the natural way must be the best way.

The truth of the matter is that in the nineteenth century, when medicinal ingredients were mostly taken from natural sources, the doctor often had the hard job of counteracting the quite serious side effects of a necessary drug with another, which in turn may have had to be counterbalanced by yet another. By refining crude drugs, or synthesising the medicinally active chemical compounds in them, the pharmaceutical industry is neither reducing the benefits of the raw material nor creating artificial substandards; it is extracting or copying the most beneficial part.

On the other hand, manufacturing medicines is, to put it crudely, big business, and the enormous variety of new and strange-sounding drugs that are produced each year by the pharmaceutical industry does not in any way reflect the number of different cures that have been discovered. It is often a case of the same thing in a different wrapping. It is the job of the pharmaceutical rep to emphasise to the doctor the benefits of his particular firm's wares as opposed to those of a rival and, in this bombardment of sales talk, the doctor himself, let alone the patient, is likely to become confused.

Of course, the doctor is aware, as most of his patients are not, that many brand names describe the same medicine, and he knows too what effects these have and the categories into which they fall. But how many doctors will know the original sources upon which the formulae they prescribe are based? And why should they? The harassed GP has enough to do, mediating between patient and specialist, separating chaff from wheat, the uncomplaining stalwart from the chronic hypochondriac. If doctors have any time at all between our claims on them and those of their interrupted family lives, it is not likely to be spent studying the ethno-botanical sources of ipecacuanha.

So, the naturopaths attempt to denigrate the pharmaceutical industry, the orthodox practitioners who prescribe that industry's products, and the products themselves (referred to as drugs, as though alternative medicines were not – which they are). They in turn are derided for their adherence to old wives' tales and their unscientific approach, which may sometimes, but by no means always, be the case. All concerned seem to miss the point, which is that there are good medicines and bad medicines, those that work and those that don't, or are inappropriately prescribed. It is useless to take sides, or to believe any one point of view. The confused patient or curious lay person might well decide that the answers will be found in unbiased textbooks.

In the preface to *Black's Medical Dictionary* there is a very valid point made, and one which should certainly be considered by all educational authorities:

> Healthy living is dependent upon knowledge of how the body works, which in turn is dependent upon an elementary knowledge of anatomy and physiology. This should, of course, be taught in our schools in the course on biology, but, as every experienced family doctor knows, even the so-called 'top people' can be incredibly ignorant on such matters.

Bravo! Presumably this worthy sentiment extends to a knowledge of the medicines we take. It is interesting to hear the responses to the question 'What do you think medicines are made of?' because the reply is so often roughly the same – 'chemicals'. Quite right. Fundamentally, all substances used as medicines can be described chemically. So can *any* substance. Suppose, then, that the curious student, wishing to understand concisely the meanings of basic medical terms and reassure himself of his general grasp of the factors involved between complaint and cure, were to begin with the basic question 'What is the definition of a medicine?' and take up *Black's Medical Dictionary*. The answer should lie somewhere between 'mediastinum' and 'medulla'. It is not there. Well then, perhaps try 'drug'. 'Drowning', 'drug addiction', 'drugs'. We are told that the sale and supply of medicines are controlled by Part 111 of the Medicines Act 1968, and that medicines should normally be sold under the supervision of a pharmacist. We do not find what drugs *per se* actually are. Maybe try 'disease'. Nothing. Perhaps the Penguin English dictionary would offer more valuable assistance:

Medicine: Substance taken internally to treat disease.
Drug: Chemical substance used in medicine, especially narcotic or stimulant; harmful substance causing addiction.

Cannot a medicine be applied externally? Is this any better than our own off-the-top-of-the-head definitions, and can these harmful substances ever be the same as those that are beneficial?

The by now flagging student may be forgiven at this juncture for brewing some coffee and lighting a cigarette, both of which contain stimulating drugs, the better to enliven the weary brain, and beginning to compare a selection of definitions taken from sources of medical reference that *do* contain the simple terms 'medicine' and 'drug':

Butterworth's Medical Dictionary
> *Medicine*: Any drug or other substance given or taken for the treatment of disease or the maintenance of health.
>
> *Drug*: Any chemical substance, synthetic or extracted from plant or animal tissue of known or unknown composition, used as a medicament to prevent or cure disease.

Penguin Medical Encyclopedia
> *Medicine*: Drug or mixture of drugs.
>
> *Drug*: In non-technical language, 'drug' has come to suggest a narcotic or habit-forming substance. In the technical sense [it] is any substance taken medicinally to help recovery from sickness or to relieve symptoms, or to modify any natural process in the body.

Concise Medical Dictionary
> *Medicine*: Any drug or preparation used for the treatment or prevention of disease, particularly a preparation that is taken by mouth.
>
> *Drug*: Any substance that affects the structure or functioning of a living organism . . . widely used for the prevention, diagnosis and treatment of disease and for the relief of symptoms. (The term 'medicine' is sometimes preferred for therapeutic drugs in order to distinguish them from narcotics and other addictive drugs that are used illegally.)

Personally, I would plump for *Butterworth's* but, when these definitions are compared, it becomes apparent that 'drug' in the colloquial sense differs considerably from the technical meaning. It also becomes clear that all the posters in our children's schools warning us and them of the dangers of drugs are not the educational optimum. Furthermore, drugs actually seem to be medicines. But are the medicines any medicines, whether they be alternative or orthodox? From what sort of plant or animal tissue are these drugs, and therefore medicines, actually derived? There are always, even in textbooks, more questions to ask.

The whole problem of doctor–patient communication seems to be compounded in this muddle. The once-curious student may close the books, rinse the coffee mugs and turn to more relaxing topics, accepting that ignorance is the lot of the lay person.

But the rewards of enquiring minds come only after they have

16

Rosehips
Rosa spp.
Rosehip syrup is commonly given to children as a source of vitamin C

been paid for by persistence and, for peace of mind and the prospect of a better understanding of things, the next time a visit to the surgery becomes necessary the student should persevere and extract from these definitions as accurate a statement as possible.

A drug can therefore be described as a substance taken directly from a naturally-occurring inorganic or organic material, but mainly the latter, or its synthetic equivalent. Additionally it can be a substance that has no counterpart in nature. In either case, it will have the effect of producing changes in or on the surface of the body and is used either non-medically, which will generally be detrimentally, or medically (then termed a medicine), and thus usually beneficially, by acting in a variety of ways to correct an imbalance of the body.

We are now in a position to consider some of these substances, their sources, how they are used and act, and how they are prepared.

Before laboratory processes of synthesis were developed, drugs obviously had to be taken from natural sources, 80 per cent of which were plants. Pharmacognosy describes the study of these sources whereas pharmacology is concerned with the way drugs act, and pharmaceutics with the preparation and compounding of them.

The logical way to describe the relationship between vegetable drugs and disease would be to start at the beginning, with sources and types of basic ingredient, the drugs they produce, how these are used and how they work to counteract our various complaints. However, to understand this in simple terms, it is probably easier to wend our way from more familiar ground and the thing we know, or should know, best – our own body and its problems. Thus we extrapolate from complaint to cure.

Most of us have some idea of the names and functions of the different parts of the body, and that the whole is a complicated chemical package parcelled up in a sturdy structure of joints and muscles, bones and skin. If asked, we may have to consider exactly where the pancreas is, but we would have a shrewd idea that it is neither in our toes nor our heads but somewhere in between, and is more than likely to be one of the internal organs. In fact, the pancreas lies behind the lower part of the stomach, and is a gland that produces in its juice four enzymes that are essential to digestion.

In mid-adulthood, after a decade or more of overdoing the intake of fats and alcohol, a person may suffer a sudden and severe pain in the abdomen, possibly coupled with an attack of vomiting. 'One of those viruses going around,' he may think. But the doctor may come to a different conclusion, and, by its features, diagnose this illness as acute pancreatitis. Apart from the obvious advice on abstension, and so long as surgery was unnecessary, the problem could be treated with an opiate drug such as pethidine, which would reduce the immediate pain and shock to the body, thus allowing natural recovery to begin.

Fortunately, pancreatitis is something only a minority of us will have to suffer; a far more common complaint is sleeplessness. Not being able to get to sleep is a particularly human problem, for other animals, unless they are in considerable discomfort, drop off with ease – an enviable trait. The problem can arise from a number of causes: cold, pain, light, noise, a chemical stimulant or anxiety. Lying in bed and worrying about something is akin to listening and talking to yourself at the same time. Although the vocal chords are not producing any sound, the brain none the less responds as if they were. In these circumstances it is worth telling yourself, very firmly, to shut up; it can sometimes work. But failing this and other home remedies – lying facing north, sipping warm milk, counting sheep – a trip to the doctor's surgery may be necessary.

If the doctor can see that counselling and assurances are not going to do the trick, he may prescribe sleeping tablets. The numbers of prescriptions (each averaging around eighty tablets) written in this country yearly are estimated in tens of millions, representing a great many sleepless nights. Sleeping tablets fall into two main categories – hypnotics and tranquillisers. Both act by depressing the brain function, the difference between them being basically a matter of degree. Hypotics simply 'bring down the hatches', rapidly inducing sleep. but a small dose has a less dramatic and more sedative effect and can be referred to as a hypnosedative. Barbiturates, for instance, derivatives of barbituric acid (so called because it was first prepared on St Barbara's Day), will have either a hypnotic or sedative action depending on the strength of the tablet. These, however, have received much criticism due to their addictive nature and a record of being over prescribed and, although they are still widely used in medicine, they are now far less frequently prescribed in the general practice. The mildly anxious insomniac is much more likely to be given one of the minor tranquillisers, which will simply relieve anxiety and so bring about a state more conducive to sleep.

Both of these examples show how drugs may be used as treatment but the pharmacological action of a drug is different from its therapeutic use. To put it more simply, drugs can be classified not just by what they do, but by the way in which they do it. Therefore, the use of a drug may be described as laxative (produces a bowel movement), anthlemintic (gets rid of worms), cardiac (has an action on the heart), febrifuge (reduces fever), sedative (is a soothing agent), vulnary (heals wounds). Drugs may act by destroying viruses, preventing disease by vaccine, altering body processes, replacing something in the body, relieving discomfort and so on. Plant drugs can also be classified according to their chemical group; for instance alkaloids, glycosides and saponins.

The source, or the bulk raw material for preparation of a

vegetable-based drug, is called the crude drug. Opium, for instance, from which can be isolated the pain killers morphine and codeine, is the dried latex from the poppy. Tea, from the leaves of a species of camellia, and coffee, derived from the berries of the sweet-smelling flowers of a laurel-type bush, both contain the heart and brain stimulant caffeine. Storax is the wonderfully soothing, cinnamon-scented resin, reminiscent of Friar's Balsam, that is exuded from the inner bark of *Liquidambar orientalis*, and is used to prepare bronchial inhalations. These crude drugs, as can be seen, may be taken from more than one part of a plant. Useful drugs may be yielded from leaves, fruits, flowers, seeds, roots, stems, barks and woods, as well as from exudates such as latexes and resins, all coming from an infinite variety of plants.

Grouping crude drugs in this way is, of course, only useful in describing their immediate features. A more accurate way of categorising them is taxonomically. Carl von Linné, a Swedish

Linnaeus in Lapland dress
Carolus Linnaeus became known as Carl von Linné after he was ennobled in 1774

20

botanist and physician, pioneered the modern form of this system in his major works of classification, *Species Plantarum* (1753) and *Systema Naturae* (1758), by which he systematically put thousands of parts of the animal, vegetable and mineral kingdoms into their appropriate places, latinising their nomenclature to avoid colloquial confusion. Taxonomy divides each kingdom into increasingly smaller groups – phylum, class, order, then family, genus and species, thereby pinpointing identification. It is only the last three categories that need concern us. By applying this system to ourselves, we can say that we are the only species (*sapiens*) remaining of a single genus (*Homo*) of a family (*Hominidae*) of the animal kingdom.

The ginkgo, or maidenhair tree, shares this solitary state by being another sole survivor, this time in the plant kingdom. Having evolved over 25,000,000 years ago, it is the last species of the one genus in its family. Generally, however, plants are more prolific. For instance, there is more to the rose family (*Rosaceae*) than the rose we know. It is only one of some ninety genera in its family, which together incorporate at least 2,000 species. In addition, not all the plants in a family have to have the same form. While some families may include only species of trees, others, such as *Rosaceae*, may include a whole range of trees, shrubs and flowers.

It may be easier to understand the relationship between genus and species if they are thought of as noun and adjective. For instance, if we take an English common name for a tree such as the red oak, the genus (*Quercus*) defines this tree as one of the oaks, and the species (*rubra*) tells us that it is a red one.

Certain features decide a genus. To stay with the familiar, the oak has in the region of 450 species, the red being one of them, and some of them share with others a similarity of leaf that makes them easily recognisable if we know the common oak leaf at all. Failing this, the unmistakable structure of the fruit, the acorn (even though there may be considerable differences in shape), is a positive clue to identification. Barks are less trustworthy; the cork oak, for instance, thick and cracked and, as the name depicts, 'corky', has little visible similarity to the less deeply crazed trunk of the common oak. It is the flowers that are by far the most reliable morphological feature of a plant in deciding how to place it taxonomically.

The fact that various drugs produced in many hundreds of plants can counteract the effects of various diseases in our bodies may seem a rather neat arrangement in our favour, but it should be remembered that the drugs which plants provide us with are often the plant's own chemical defence against its environment.

To put all these factors into context, the following are but a few examples of particular plants and their curative properties.

'Naked ladies treat portly gent' has the sound of a Sunday newspaper scandal. But naked ladies is one of the common names applied to *Colchicum autumnale*, more familiarly known as autumn crocus. The portly, bewigged gentleman with the walking stick, portrayed in nineteenth-century caricatures, traditionally suffered from gout. This disease is generally associated with over-indulgence, often as a result of which acute pain and swelling in the big toe make walking a misery, and later other joints can also become affected. Apart from staying away from rich foods, beer and port and resting the gouty leg, treatment by the drug colchicine may be prescribed. This is an alkaloid found in *Colchicum* seeds and corms which relieves pain and inflammation within a few hours, but side effects are vomiting or diarrhoea. Another drug derived from colchicine is demecolcine, used to treat a form of leukaemia.

Autumn Crocus
Colchicum autumnale
Also known as 'Naked Ladies' as they flower without leaves. A traditional cure for gout.

Purging Cassia
Cassia fistula
Cassia pods are the dried ripe fruits of a large tree, indigenous to India,
now widely cultivated in the tropics

There was a time when senna pods were a common theme of music hall humour. They were a favourite home-brew laxative, widely used for children during the 1950s, but sennoside preparations are still one of the commonest prescribed drugs for this purpose. Senna leaf and pods usually come from the two species *Cassia senna* and *Cassia angustifolia*, known respectively as Alexandrian and Tinnevelly senna. The chief constituents of senna are the sennosides which are phenolic glycosides, producing their desired effect by irritating the lining of the bowel and stimulating it to contract.

Digitalis is the crude drug provided by the dried leaves of the ordinary purple foxglove (*Digitalis purpurea*), and from which is derived digitoxin. The white foxglove (*Digitalis lanata*) yields both digitoxin and the faster-acting digoxin. Both these drugs, pharmaceutically described as cardiac glycosides, are used to treat congestive heart failure by causing the heart muscles to work more efficiently thus reducing the volume of blood accumulated in the heart chambers while its action is relaxed. The inefficient circulation of the blood, due to this disease, can cause fluid retention in the body, so these drugs, by improving circulation and allowing the kidneys to work more effectively, can be considered secondarily as diuretics, although they would not be used solely for this purpose. Digoxin has come to be one of the most widely used drugs for this type of heart failure, and each year the foxglove yields many thousands of kilograms of its leaves to our advantage. This is worth remembering the next time the tidy hedge-trimmers in Wales and the West Country are seen slicing these pretty flowers to their roots in order to keep the side roads clear for the holiday traffic in early summer.

Finally, drugs take, or may be taken in, a number of different forms. Crude vegetable drugs, as we have seen, come in whatever form the plant produces them – roots or resins, berries or bark. Their active constituents can be extracted directly from this form by infusions, made in the same way as we brew tea, or decoctions, where the more unwilling barks or roots may have to be boiled in liquid for some time before cooling and straining. Prepared drugs can take the form of liquid or solid extracts, tinctures, pills, tablets, capsules or suppositories. Capsules are conveniently-sized containers for oily drugs and acrid tastes. Pills can be made by mixing powdered substances with a viscous liquid and rolling this into small spherical masses. Tablets, which are far more common, are made by compressing drugs into a conveniently small form, which has the advantage of accurate dosage and more rapid absorption.

There are four major ways in which drugs can be administered. They can be applied to the skin as creams or ointments, or to the mucous membranes which line the hollow organs of the body. They can be inhaled. They can be taken by mouth or via the rectum. Finally, they can be injected: into a nerve, as in dentistry; into the spinal cord; intravenously (into a vein); intramuscularly (into a muscle); or subcutaneously (under the skin).

The array of drugs that we encounter during our lives takes such various forms that it is easy to lose sight of their origins. In primitive societies the medicine man may well have obscured these so as to guard his secrets; in developed societies their disguise is due to modern manufacture. Whatever society we are a part of, it does no good for the constituents or the action of a drug to be a mystery to the one who takes it.

2

Plants and Primitives

Ever since Asclepius, Greek god of the healing arts, delegated the responsibility of mixing his medicines to Hygieia, there has been a distinction between the one who prescribes and the one who prepares the prescription. However, in primitive societies, the doctor is his own pharmacist and more besides. Roles ranging from healer to executioner are inclusive to the one of general spiritual adviser, which was inaugurated by the common belief that matters of concern, including disease, where the cause was not understood or the outcome was unpredictable were all subject to supernatural influence and should therefore be dealt with in the same way and by the same individual whose powers had necessarily to be magical.

We each have our own image of the fully-fledged medicine man, resplendent in his parrot feathers, painted and garish as he performs his confusion of rituals, around him hovering a host of hallucinations, or sitting hunched in his baboon-skin vestments beside Lake Tanganyika, tossing bones as oracle in his role as diagnostician. His type comes in many guises, each of them apparently a world apart from our own familiar GP. But the majority of his cures, as well as the poisons and elixirs he brews to transport himself into a suitably altered state to perform his magical rituals, are based on the chemical compounds found in plants. These are basic to most medicines throughout the world, whether taken in their crude form, or with a glass of water after being synthesised and reduced to the neat 'three times a day' capsule, and have been used to effect changes in our bodies, for better or worse, during the entire history of our species. To understand how this use developed, we must look to its origins.

Among the relics of the earliest humans have sometimes been found traces of the plants they used. These are valuable, and often the only, clues to the environment and behaviour of our pre-historic ancestors of the palaeolithic or Old Stone Age.

Wood charcoal provides a permanent record, where wood has been used as fuel or deliberately exposed to fire for other purposes, for example, hardening spears. Wood may also be preserved in very dry conditions, for instance in caves, or in soils that have become waterlogged and not exposed to the air, as in bogs or lakesides. Its use in construction is evident, and whittled stakes may have been used for fencing posts. Wooden spears are more tentatively identified, but digging sticks have been found in association with several palaeolithic sites, particularly in Africa.

Although the fragile structures of plants' flowers and fibres do not stand the test of time so well as woody plants, their pollen does. Where pollen is amassed in conditions and distributions that appear out of context, it indicates deliberate collection as opposed to accidental depositing. Clusters of grass pollens, for instance, suggest the use of straw for bedding or other light furnishings, and the remains of seeds and nuts are useful in determining the types of food that were available.

The evidence of plants used as medicine in the Old Stone Age is mainly indirect. We may deduce from the intelligent activity displayed in the use of plants for other purposes that there may also have been practised the 'making of medicine' in advance of necessity, or by traditional, as opposed to instinctive, prescription as the need arose. Signs of the diseases and injuries from which our early ancestors suffered are inscribed on their bones. In some cases healing has occurred and it is not unlikely that fractures could have been assisted in this by the application of splints or poultices. In other cases, the deformed bones of some individuals show that they would have been disabled for years before eventual death, so they apparently had been cared for and tolerated by other members of their group, and possibly treated by them. Of course, we like to view ministering to the sick as a display of human kindness and caring. Sadly, it is more likely to be one of sense rather than sentiment. Acts of altruism assist a society that depends upon the co-operation of its members for survival, and preserving the life of each member of a small, interdependent family group is beneficial to its total strength. Even a partially-abled body is better than a dead one in a society where numbers count, and those that practised the healing of their sick would have had a selective advantage over those that did not.

But while we may assume that medicine was practised in the Old Stone Age, we must scratch about for proof. It is possible that grinding stones were used mortar-and-pestle-style to pre-pare medicines, but they are equally as likely to have been used in the preparation of food. To find more direct evidence, we must dig deeper.

As recently as 1951, the medicine of the Old Stone Age was still a blank page in medical history. In his book of that year on the subject, Dr Henry Sigerist of Yale University wrote: 'We have no evidence whatsoever of any palaeolithic medicine . . . dis-appointed, we turn to the New Stone Age.' In the same year this was published, the archaeologist Ralph Solecki began the pre-liminary surveys of a cave in north-east Iraq. It was called Shanidar, and the finds there were to become something of a sensation.

The explorations began in May 1951 in the Zagros Mountains, where Solecki hoped to find evidence of Stone Age dwellings among the caves there. After a month of fruitless probings into dingy and unlikely-looking caves, he decided on a quicker and simpler approach: he asked the locals. These were the semi-nomadic Kurds, who were able to tell him of the Big Cave of Shanidar, which they used themselves as a refuge while their herds were grazing. Once located it was, Solecki said, 'the most magnificent cave' that he had found so far. Large and airy, with a huge south-facing entrance which allowed the sun to keep it well lit, and the earth floor dry, it seemed a perfect dwelling place. In fact it was inhabited when he got there, as it had been on and off for 60,000 years or more – although he did not know this at the time. It was the obvious place to start excavations, once the temporary occupants had moved on.

Solecki returned to the cave in the autumn, and the digging began. At a depth of about five feet into the cave floor, the earth began to yield up its treasures; these were modest – some stone chippings and a little charcoal – and, aged approximately 10,000 years, comparatively 'modern'. It was enough, however, to justify a more ambitious project. This took time to organise, but by the late spring of 1953 it was well under way. On 22 June, the remains of an infant were unearthed. The Shanidar Baby, as it was nicknamed, was estimated to be around 60,000 years old and was classified as a Neanderthal. It was an exciting find, and more than Solecki had hoped for, but with some luck perhaps the mother and father also would be found near by. With this objective in mind, Solecki visited the cave for a third time, late in 1956.

On 27 April 1957, his team discovered the remains of a second Neanderthal, on this occasion an adult male who, judging by his skeletal injuries, appeared to have met his death in a rockslide or by falling. A month later two further adult males were found, one of whom was not immediately identified as human.

Finally, in August 1960, 'while trimming a dangerous-looking bulge in the cave wall', Solecki made his most important find, although its significance was not fully understood until eight years later. It was another male and became known as Shanidar 4. Before the excavations were complete, a fifth male, two adult females and a second infant were recovered from the site, bringing the total number of bodies to nine.

Discoveries as important as these are subjected to the most critical of inspections. Bones must be dated, diseases diagnosed, injuries explained and the surrounding soil analysed. As a result of these tests, three particularly interesting facts became apparent. Firstly, this had not been one 'big, happy family'. Three of the males had died thousands, perhaps even tens of thousands, of years after the other six individuals. Secondly, the fact that two of the more recent group had been considerably disabled some years before death and that members of both groups had received burials provided further evidence that the Neanderthals were not the violent and idiotic brutes it had once been thought they were. They were in fact intelligent and caring.

The third, and most important, discovery came from the soil. In 1968 Solecki sent some soil samples taken from around Shanidar 4 to Arlette Leroi-Gourhan in Paris. She had been the team's palaeobotanist for several years, but until then had discovered nothing of any great importance. Immediately, these latest samples appeared different. Of the twenty-eight species she was able to identify by their pollen, seven were grouped in obvious clusters which appeared to have been woven into the branches of a pine-like shrub. Although the practice of Neanderthal burial had been recognised since 1924, and various animal bones found in association with the graves (in one case a set of six goat horns placed in a rough circle) had suggested that certain funeral rites had been observed, the Shanidar burial was unprecedented in archaeology and as startling as it was unique – for these were the

Hollyhock
Althaea rosea
Fifty thousand years ago, these appear to have been collected for a
Neanderthal wreath

fragments of a wreath. This was not all, for when these flowers were described a still more significant fact emerged; namely that all were well known and still used for their medicinal properties.

The plants found in the Shanidar wreath are commonly known as yarrow, groundsel, cornflower, St Barnaby's thistle, grape hyacinth and hollyhock. The seventh plant, a type of woody horsetail from which the drug ephedrine is derived, did not actually form part of the wreath and it is thought that it had been used as a soft base upon which to lay the corpse, as its stems lend themselves well to bedding. The name yarrow is derived from the Anglo-Saxon word meaning healer. The plant is named *Achillea* in Latin, after the Greek hero Achilles, who is said to have used it to heal the wounds of the soldiers who fought with him in the Trojan Wars. Solecki describes the hollyhock as the poor man's aspirin, and it is tempting to make the connection here between its curative properties and the fact that the Neanderthals are known to have been martyrs to arthritis.

Even Solecki, a scientist and not given to jumping to conclusions, speculated that 'Shanidar 4 was not only a very important man, a leader, but may also have been a kind of medicine
man or Shaman in his group.' However, we must judge for
ourselves whether this was a deliberate application of the science
of pharmacy or an astonishing coincidence. In support of the
former, it should be noted that had these plants been gathered for
purely decorative purposes there would have been other, far
brighter and more abundant blooms at hand. From the singular
distribution of the hollyhock alone, Leroi-Gourhan concluded
that more than 50,000 years ago some person or persons had
ranged the mountainsides in the mournful task of collecting these
one by one. Solecki writes: 'Taken altogether, these flowers from
the Shanidar grave certainly do not look like the ornamental
group one familiarly finds in the home parlour.'

I am inclined to agree with his view, but would also like to note
the following. A couple of weeks prior to my reading the details
of the finds at Shanidar, I picked some remnants of the thick
summertime carpet of wild flowers which grows on my favourite

Tansy
Tanacetum vulgare
Golden-yellow 'bitter buttons' flower between July and September

Thameside pasture. Three of the species were potential medicines, but I brought them home simply because I like the look of
yarrow, tansy and rosehips together in a vase with a backing of
aspen . . . Whatever conclusions we draw from the Shanidar
wreath, we are bound to recognise its connotations of ceremony.
Whereas simple burial can be seen merely as a practicality, burial
with flowers implies funeral rites which, more than a memorial
gesture, indicate a belief in an afterlife.

Although the Neanderthals may have had medicine, they
lacked the one factor that the later Cro-Magnons had which
assured human supremacy on earth. Not more brains (the Neanderthals had larger brains than modern *Homo sapiens*), but a
slightly different anatomical structure that lifted the tilt of the
head, straightening out the sloping brow and lengthening the
vocal tract, thus enabling them to produce the sound that is so
familiar to us – the human voice. This is not to say that the
Neanderthals could not communicate with one another – they
undoubtedly could – but that the Cro-Magnons had a range of
sound which superseded the nasal and limited speech of their
predecessors. While language may label items and incidents, it
also creates beliefs and ideas. The Cro-Magnons did not sit and
think in silence until a word was unanimously agreed upon to
describe their thoughts. Beliefs are the result of discussion and, as
social communities and language became more complex, so did
the range of human concepts.

These were given expression in the graphic images of the cave
paintings which are first associated with the Cro-Magnon culture. Beautifully and skilfully executed though these are, they are
seldom seen as art for art's sake. They are too specific, almost
invariably depicting the prey of the hunter: the wild-life upon
which the community depended. The paintings are presumed to
be a part of some magical ritual that guaranteed successful
hunting and the subsequent well-being of the tribe. The fact that
many of them decorate the walls deep inside the cave complex,
away from those areas which provided community shelter, adds
to their mystery and hints at the secrecy and hidden nature of the
medicine man's craft.

An image still haunts a Pyrenean cave where, painted some
20,000 years ago, there is a figure bedecked in the skin and antlers
of a deer. This above all seems to beg us believe our eyes, and do
the medicine man's dignity the honour of accepting his profession's venerability. It is as if he is saying, 'Look, I have always

been here.' But in the modern world we are taught not to trust appearances alone, so we must be careful not to presume too much. Perhaps these paintings were simply a part of some initiation ceremony of the young hunter, to show him the weak spots of his potential quarry; for, whatever the degree of ritualistic element, one thing is certain – these people knew their anatomy. Sinew, muscle, hide and bone structure became almost caricature with the increasing confidence of the master's stroke.

Less than delicate but none the less eloquent in its directness is the Pindal Mammoth, painted between 20,000 and 30,000 years ago with red ochre on a cave wall in northern Spain. It is a simple, heavily outlined side view of the beast with an unmistakable 'blob' at its centre which, if a little on the large side, seems certainly to represent a heart. Although the late palaeolithic understanding of the human body structure may have been based on the anatomical knowledge of the butcher, by the neolithic era this had developed into the surgical skill that allowed for the performing of trephining. This entails the removal of a circular or oval portion of the cranium and is practised nowadays to relieve pressure on the brain or to allow for the removal of growths, or splinters in the case of fractures.

The first prehistoric trephined skulls were unearthed in France in 1685, but it was nearly 200 years later that the holes in them were recognised as the deliberate incisions of flint knives in the first successful attempts at this operation. The process was referred to in the writings of the ancients and practised by primitive cultures of Europe, America and the Pacific until modern times, usually for the purpose of 'release' – either of the intrusive pain of the chronic headache, or the malevolent spirits invading the bodies of the insane, epileptic or paralysed.

Although trephining deals with the application of surgery as opposed to pharmacy, it demonstrates two general points: firstly that neolithic medicine was more than a simple hit or miss affair, and secondly that it incorporated the basic concept that disorders of the body are spirit-orientated. As proof of the former point, in 1962 a Peruvian brain surgeon, Francisco Grana, successfully accomplished this operation using prehistoric instruments to show their effectiveness. Also in the 1960s, the spiritual connotations of the operation were revived by a Dutchman, Dr Bart Hugues. His teachings culminated in the extraordinary daring of a young Chelsea couple who attempted to raise their consciousness by boring into their skulls with an electric drill. They not only succeeded in this foolhardy recourse to enlightenment, but claim to have continued living in a perpetual state of heightened 'awareness'. The details of their story are not for the squeamish, but the gist of it not only reflects a primitive concept, but says much for the gullibility which extends into 'civilised' societies of those who will go to surprising lengths beyond the boundaries of common sense on the say-so of 'the doctor'. So, before we scoff at the superstition that may set the victim of a witchdoctor's curse into a fatal panic, we would do well to consider what our own feelings would be if we were faced with a specialist's announcement that we were on the mortal shortlist. And the primitive does not often have the benefit of a second opinion.

With the neolithic age also came the point of departure from the sole reliance on plants that were naturally available and conveniently gathered. In Europe, the melting glaciers and the warmer climate brought humankind out of the rocky shelters and down to the lakesides where, once the necessity of hunting had been replaced by the domestication of livestock, the ways of the

Oats
Avena sativa
During the neolithic age permanent communities were formed and agricultural life blossomed

wanderer could be abandoned and the lifestyle of hunter–gatherer exchanged for that of fisherman–farmer.

With fresh water 'on tap', permanent communities were formed and agricultural life blossomed. With it came the oldest and most permanent medicine we know: the poppy. Its seeds have been found among the remains of Swiss lakeside settlements and similar regions throughout the neolithic Bronze and Copper Ages and, while poppyseed oil has long been used for nutritional and economic purposes, it is unlikely that the narcotic effects of the poppy went unnoticed during this span of time. Opium has been seen as both bane and blessing to our kind throughout history, but it can only be viewed fairly in direct accordance with the way in which it is used. As a multi-purpose panacea, it deals

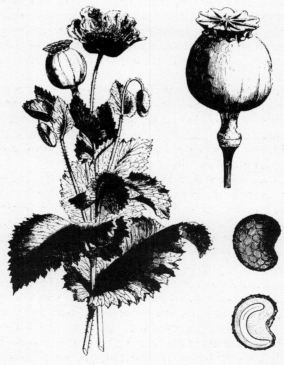

Poppy
Papaver somniferum
Both bane and blessing throughout history

with disease and injury at the most basic level, by relieving suffering. Taken as a narcotic, it induces a drifting and careless somnolence that dulls the senses to the dangers of its destructiveness. Indifferent to its powers, the poppy flowers on across gravel, garden and grave.

It is thought that at this stage of early agriculture, the plant lore and cults that were later to flourish in most primitive societies took root, although not as a direct result of agriculture, but rather as a consequence of the social behaviour that it effected. Similarly, the time was ripe for the primitive Shaman as mediator between magic and medicine to materialise fully and elaborate on a theme already conceptualised by his cave-dwelling predecessors. This is not to say that the medicine man developed only with agricultural societies; he was present among the Neanderthals, and the Bushmen of Africa and the aboriginal tribes of Australia are only two existing examples of lower hunters who live by gathering rather than cultivating, yet who still have their doctors. However, it is clearer to see how social niches were provided for his prototype in societies where agriculture developed.

Home from the hills, the menfolk were granted the new luxury of leisuretime. After a little fishing and a stroll round the livestock, plenty of time remained for discussion and debate, and where their roles as warriors and hunters were partly redundant, they could reassert their dominant status by taking control of religious and political affairs.

Much of what is important in primitive societies is dependent on natural causes – the climate, which can bring feast or famine, changes in location, or social conditions which may precipitate the sudden spread of disease – but because these causes are not fully understood they are explained as mystical occurrences. To help decide issues associated with these, primitive societies throughout history have turned to the narcotic and hallucinogenic properties of certain plants which, because of their power, are always treated with a respect that is also extended to whoever presides over the rituals and cults formed around them. Similarly, neolithic debating parties may also have discovered that certain plant substances, offering more than simply food for thought, had the effect of transporting the senses into mystical realms, where the deities that controlled the fate of their communities could be met on common ground.

Meanwhile, fieldwork is often women's work. Cooking is

too. Whichever sex today dons the apron to take up position at the family stove, it cannot be denied that the concept of 'the one who feeds the baby also feeds the family' is entrenched in all human cultures. The cultivation of crops for food rather than for marketing is the grass roots equivalent of going out and doing the shopping. Again, the hand that stirs the pot is usually the one to pick the ingredients.

In societies of hunter–gatherers, it is usually the woman's task to gather the plants. Similarly, in the early stages of agriculture it would have been her task to tend and plant them. It would have been up to her to decide what was cultivated and what was not, and if a particular plant seemed beneficial to her children, or to the aged and ailing left in her charge, she would have been more likely to pay particular attention to its care.

We may therefore wonder why the one who came to preside as specialist over serious injury and disease would be a man. Even today, the concept of man as doctor and woman as nurse persists, despite the fact that everyone knows and accepts that the roles are interchangeable. From the point of view of surgery, this is not difficult to understand. Major operations are, in any case, rare in primitive societies, but where the role of surgeon was adopted it was as an extension to that of warrior and hunter. In the ferocity of battle or the hunt, aid would have been given to the injured by those immediately at hand. This was not the first-aid for which we earn our badges at school; these were desperate measures for desperate situations and, although action was no doubt taken in compassion, there would have been no time for sentiment or deliberation over necessary amputations or suturing of wounds.

Crude surgical knowledge learnt in these situations provided the foundation for the skills later to be refined on the home front, as exemplified in the practice of trephining, and demonstrated to their full extent in more recent times by an operation witnessed in 1879 by a Dr Robert Felkin during his travels in Uganda. A perfect Caesarean section was performed on a first-time mother, anaesthetised only with copious amounts of banana wine, and a healthy child delivered from a wound which, stitched and disinfected, healed in less than two weeks. Of course, here in particular, few women, even the invaluable midwife, would have been able to muster sufficient confidence to perform such surgery, when the patient could well be her own daughter or younger sister, and so although women were spared the experience of the often gruesome circumstances responsible for serious injury it

36

was at the expense of being considered unworthy to deal with it, and one which confined their surgical abilities to the cutting of umbilical cords for thousands of years.

On a pathological level too, because the cause of serious disease was unlikely to have been understood, it would have become one of those mystical issues dealt with by the menfolk and specifically by the one who claimed, or was considered by the others, to have the most influence in this field.

It would be nice to think that the medicine man's motives for accepting responsibility in serious medical matters were founded on patriarchal concern for his followers, but they probably were not. His foremost role, as general spiritual adviser, would have

Medicine Man of the Arhouaque Indians, Columbia
The majority of the medicine man's cures are found in the chemical compounds present in plants

given him a personal power which he would have been more than willing to extend to medicine, once his suitability had been generally agreed upon. This power, though primarily instated and retained through his patients' belief in the supernatural and in his control over it, had to be seen to be effective. He could not afford to have his prestigious status in society challenged by losing face and, for his role to have evolved, he must certainly have accumulated a range of reliable and naturally available remedies that were genuinely beneficial. He may have arrived at their application by trial and error, but they gave proof to his practice, thereby securing the confidence of his patients, upon which his position depended.

Speculations on the evolution of the medicine man are largely based on what we know today of his role and its history in more recent primitive communities. It is generally believed to have begun at the hunter–gatherer stage, developed in the neolithic and Bronze Ages, and to be closely allied to magic. We know also that the neolithic lake dwellers cultivated over 200 plant species, including the poppy and vervain, both medicinal, and that from this age twirls the Shaman of northern Asia, whose similarity to the North American Indian medicine man of the Queen Charlotte Island area of British Columbia is too striking not to be seen as of common descent.

We can fairly generalise too about the social conditions in prehistoric times that established his prestigious position and his personal motives for accepting it. But since then the human race and its environment have become so diverse that no single latter-day example of a Shaman, medicine man or witchdoctor would accurately describe their common ancestor. However, to complete a picture of him as a general type, we can look at those practices which, by their universality, may be assumed to be inherited from the same source.

There is, however, one area of differentiation which should first be taken into account, namely the various attitudes to the sick and towards disease among primitive communities. These are bound to differ according to the degree of disadvantage that sickness brings to the community as a whole. Whereas it may have been in the best interests of the Neanderthals to care for their sick, this has not always been the case in subsequent cultures. Abandonment, starvation and murder have also been the lot of the ill or dying. The Kubu, in the forests of Sumatra, fled disease when it reached epidemic proportions, those that were still untouched simply moving on, deeper into the forest. The Nava-ho and Hopi Indians did not hesitate in doing the same. Eskimo elders have patiently frozen to death on ice floes, left to their fate by their families with whom they could no longer keep pace. Often, where there was famine, the sick were the first to be denied food, so their end was hastened by starvation. These may seem to us inhumane attitudes, but they are practical, and dictated by circumstance. It was not for want of maternal instinct that a mother in many primitive societies would immediately deprive her newborn child of life, if its birth followed too closely on its sibling's heels. She did it out of concern for the child still suckling.

Alternatively, those that survived serious illness were often esteemed for their close brush with the spirit world, and follow-ing their return to good health were elected as medical deputies. There is a certain logic in this. In any modern hospital ward, there are two types of medical authority to be found: the one who does the rounds, and the one who is examined. The expertise of the latter may be singularly specialised, but it is founded on first-hand experience. In particular, the Ojibwa tribe of North American Indians used this as one of their selection systems for admission into their Grand Medicine Society, which once boasted as many as 1,000 members.

One thing is certain, and it is that primitive societies do not breed hypochondriacs. Coughs, colds and temporary aches and pains are not usually considered worth troubling the medicine man with. The Mano of Liberia, for instance, have long under-stood and uncomplainingly accepted toothache, cases of small-pox or measles, bites from insects or animals and their subsequent infection, merely observing that 'everyone has them'.

There are, of course, differing ideas among societies about what can be commonly remedied and what requires special treatment, but at whatever stage it is decided that the specialist is needed the cry is unanimously for the medicine man. And he comes with a song and a prayer and a deal of ritual and ceremony.

We know that the effects of the drugs in some plants on our thoughts and feelings are physical ones, and that they are the result of a particular plant's chemistry working on our own. The medicine man believes that these effects are non-physical, and that they are the result of the plant's magical properties working wonders on his mind. He takes an opposite approach yet, by the association, converges with the rational.

Before healing others, the medicine man's philosophy is 'physician first treat thyself', and he prepares to pronounce prognosis and prescribe treatment by getting himself into a suitable state, either by energetic activity and dancing, or, more simply, by using the plants that alter consciousness to lift his own spirit to another plane. Colloquially it is known as getting high, and is the practice often shared by other tribesmen in debate, in preparation for battle, for initiation into manhood or just as celebration.

'One side will make you grow taller and the other will make you grow shorter,' the Caterpillar told Alice after removing the hookah from his mouth. A little nibble of the mushroom to which he had referred and, the next thing she knew, her chin had struck her foot. Alice was hallucinating again, or dreaming, as Lewis Carroll had it, but it is very likely that some of the strange sensory distortions he had Alice encounter in her Wonderland were based on accounts he had read of the fly agaric mushroom in a book published in 1862, only three years before his own – *A Plain and Easy Account of British Funghi*, by M. C. Cook. The white-spotted red mushroom is a familiar illustration to many a fairy tale and it is as appropriate as it is decorative, for it is thought to be one of the most anciently used hallucinogens. It is common in northern temperate regions of both hemispheres, but the origins of its use are most frequently associated with the Siberian Shamans who shared with their tribesmen the experience of the delightful sensations and colourful visions that it induced. It had

Fly Agaric
Amanita muscaria
Thought to be one of the most anciently used hallucinogens

the added attraction of being an economic intoxicant too, because its active principles remain practically unchanged after excretion from the body; it was the custom of some to recycle its effects by drinking the urine of those who had imbibed before.

From the warmer climate of equatorial Africa comes the plant *Iboga*, yielding from its roots the powerful stimulant ibogaine. Widely used by tribes and secret societies in the Gabon and Congo, it has been used both by hunting parties as a means of staving off hunger, and, in larger doses, to conjure up visions of the plant-god Bwiti during initiation into his cult.

The reason why a greater variety of hallucinogenic plants has been used and recorded in the New World rather than anywhere else remains a puzzle to the experts but, as it does not seem to be a matter of distribution, it is probably one of cultural inheritance; certainly the comparatively sophisticated Aztecs passed on a thing or two to their more primitive descendants, peyote for example. The appearance of this stumpy little cactus gives no hint of the spectacular visions its 'mescal button' produces, nor of the numerous cults it has inspired throughout its native Mexico and among Indians as far north as Canada. No amount of missionary zeal was able to stamp out the respect for its deity, Mescalito, and even those that were persuaded to adopt the Christian doctrines merely relegated him to the status of Saint Nino de Peyotl.

The *conquistadores*, notorious for their persuasive methods of instilling Christian ethics into those Indian societies whose destruction they managed to justify, had as little success in controlling the ritual use of the Aztecs' 'flesh of the gods', for psilocybe mushrooms, their action very similar in effect to peyote, are still used ceremonially by several tribes of Mexican Indians. Still sacred to Mexican Indians too, particularly in the south, are the seeds of two species of morning glory, one of which is the ololiuqui of the Aztecs. Both are used for pseudo-medical and religious purposes in nearly all Oaxacan communities, containing as they do lysergic acid, popularly known to us as LSD. Further north, in Mexico, New Mexico and Texas, the red bean cult flourished for centuries before it was abandoned for the 'safer' peyote.

A snuff, known by one of its names as epena, made from the bark resin of the virola tree and other ingredients, is habitually sniffed by all the males of the Iticoteri and other tribes of the jungle regions between Venezuela and Brazil. In eastern Colombia, however, it is the sole prerogative of the Shaman.

From the same family (*Solanaceae*) as belladonna, mandrake and henbane, so popular with European witches of the Middle Ages, and containing chemicals in common with them, comes datura, which grows in several regions of Europe, Asia and South America, but is used particularly among Indian tribes from the south-western United States. It takes its common name, jimson weed, after an incident in Jamestown in 1676, when soldiers, there to put down a colonial rebellion, were waylaid by its effects for several days.

Thus mentally prepared, the medicine man can think about the best method of treatment, and he may choose either magical or empirical; non-rational or rational. In his non-rational treatments can be seen a practice as old as medicine itself. This is quackery, which is seldom a simple approach and often something of a performance, its dramatics enacted with the objective of keeping the audience spellbound, and its success dependent on its not turning into a tragedy. To raise the question of quackery is not to be derogatory to the medicine man's profession once the subtle distinction between a quack and a charlatan has been defined. The former is often well-intentioned and quite unaware that his claims are bogus; the latter invariably knows his are.

The first step towards any treatment is diagnosis, but the medicine man's role as diagnostician is equally one of diviner and detective. The concept of Intrusion is almost universal in primitive societies, the rationale behind this being that disease is an

Deadly Nightshade
Atropa belladonna
Also known as belladonna. Popular with European witches of the Middle Ages.

Jimson Weed
Datura stramonium
Named after an incident in Jamestown in 1676

object or malevolent spirit which has been magically introduced to the body either by a living enemy or an ancestral ghost with a score to settle. So, as he already knows that something has intruded that shouldn't be there, what the medicine man has first to find out is who, physical or otherwise, put it there.

Sometimes he delegates the responsibility for discovering this to an assistant specialist, but more often than not he sets about it himself; not with a microscope, of course, but with an oracle. Throwing palm kernels in the air, catching them and then reading the results is about as reliable as reading tea leaves, but to the Yoruba of Nigeria these results are taken as seriously as we take the ones that come back from the pathology lab to our GP. Farther south in Africa, the Bantu preference was for throwing bones; and north again, the Azande of Sudan still use their all-purpose oracle, the rubbing board, which answers a straight yes or no depending on whether its wetted flat lid sticks or runs smoothly over the board's surface after it has been spread with fruit juice.

Although these methods may seem less than certain, none of them is directly harmful. The same cannot be said for diagnosis by ordeal poison, which is administered on a policy similar to the sink-or-swim method of judging suspected witches in the Dark Ages. If those accused of harming their ailing neighbour were guilty, they took their calabar bean and died. If they were innocent, they vomited and purged themselves of all blame. How many innocent victims have succumbed to this misguided jurisdiction we dare not guess, but we may wonder what number of those who were actually guilty of having a hand in the removal of a rival were absolved on the strength of their stomach rather than their moral fibre.

The calabar bean grows on a woody climber by rivers in West Africa, and comes safely packaged in a pod, like the more familiar of its family (*Leguminosae*), the garden pea and runner bean. Also in West and Central Africa, an infusion from sassy bark was brewed for the unfortunate defendant prior to ordeal trials. Other plants used in this form of crude justice were *Strychnos nux-vomica*, particular to tropical areas of Africa, and, to the east, *Strophanthus kombé* and *Acokanthera veneta*. Farther east across the globe, sap from the bark of the upas tree was the favourite ordeal poison, as the tanguin nut was in Madagascar. Naturally, the notoriety of these plants led to their subsequent analysis, and from the calabar bean physostigmine was isolated. As a poison it brings general paralysis but, as a medicine, made into eye drops, it will contract the pupil and reduce pressure on the eyeball. *Strychnos nux-vomica*, as the generic name suggests, is a source of strychnine, and from *Strophanthus* and *Acokanthera* species come Strophanthin-K and -G respectively (commonly called ouabain), both forms having the effect of stimulating the heart in an action comparable to digitalis.

But there is a part that some of these plants played in hunting and warfare that was more accurate and deadly than the one they had in Russian roulette-style trials, when the victim had at least a hope of survival. The fear of intrusion was realised in the darts

Nux Vomica
Strychnos nux-vomica
Contains the powerful poison strychnine

and arrows tipped with poisoned barbs that flew fleet and silent to their targets – and there was no second chance, except on those rare occasions when the marksman's aim was faulty. In East and South Africa, species of *Acokanthera* provided the poison for these fatal missiles. The red oil from the pounded seeds of a species of *Strophanthus* was smeared on Zulu spears and both the upas tree and sassy bark had dual roles in their regions. One arrow poison has a dark and secret history that pharmacists took many years to unravel. Curare is the name not of a plant, but of a lethal mixture of several poisons depending on the region, and is most commonly associated with South America. Although it sometimes contained such virulent substances as insect poison, snake venom and decaying flesh, its major ingredients were usually either *Strychnos toxifera* or *Chondrodendron tomentosum*.

Calabash curare, sent in hollow gourds from Guyana, Venezuela and Colombia, was once the most commercial form and contained mostly strychnos. Tube curare, packed in bamboo, came from the upper Amazon and was made chiefly from *Chondrodendron tomentosum*. From this tubocurarine was first isolated, which is still entered in the British Pharmacopoeia and used as a muscle relaxant during surgery – a far cry from its origins and the tale told of its original preparation when the oldest women of the tribe were made to mix it in closed huts. If after the second day these unfortunate 'pharmacists' were not dead from the fumes of the mixture, the prescription was deemed to be not of optimum potency, and their penalty was perseverance unto a grim and inevitable end.

As for the actual treatment of disease, taking preventive measures may seem to be one of the medicine man's more rational attitudes. However, although his theory may be sound, his measures are rather less so. Amulets (which can be almost any item to which the medicine man attributes magical powers) ward off disease, talismans bring good health – not very scientific, but then neither are our familiar and accepted horseshoes, four-leafed clovers or St Christopher medals. As a type of amulet, the Nicobarese would stand an effigy called a Kareau outside the patient's hut, with the intention of frightening away the spirits of disease. If the patient recovered, this was seen to have been effective. If the patient did not recover, the effigy was destroyed. The Iroquois Indians of the Queen Charlotte Islands used a Thunderbird Rattle for the same purpose. In fact, making a song and dance and a general deal of noise was a favourite preventive measure of many of the North American Indian tribes, in particular the Apaches and Cherokees.

Finally, where disease has entered despite these various measures, it must of course be removed. This has often been effected by Sympathetic Magic, where the desired result is imitated – a method akin to sticking pins in dolls. This particular form of magic was, incidentally, often believed to be the means by which disease could be introduced by an enemy's taking nail clippings or hair from a victim, or making an effigy of him and cursing it. Similarly, as a cure, Sympathetic Magic could be applied in the same way.

Another method of magically removing disease is by transference, which, as the name implies, is simply ritually transferring the disease to something else, be it an animal (in which case the creature is then destroyed), or a plant, as exemplified by the practice in European folk medicine of passing a sick person through a split holly or willow sapling. It is in the process of 'removal' that the medicine man in many tribes most conspicuously displays the talents of a real showman. By sleight of hand he may palm a bone or small object and, after rubbing the afflicted area of his patient, reveal this as the cause of complaint. Alternatively, he may suck out the disease through a tube, as practised by the Ojibwa Indians of North America.

But this is also where magic merges with reason, and the irrational approach meets with the desired effect. For instance, if opium was administered to entice the tormenting entities out of the unfortunate migraine sufferer, the evident relief that this gave would have guaranteed its repeated use. A case of the right remedy for the wrong reasons, but nevertheless effective. A particular example of this misinterpretation of plant use was practised by the Mano of Liberia. Their doctors used hot plant poultices to draw out the intrusive spirits doing damage to their patients, and, hey presto, they vanished as the pain subsided.

However, there is one universal practice that exemplifies the crossover between superstition and reason above all others, and is based on observing the phenomena of parasitism. Often the intrusive spirits of disease were regarded as some devilish and phantom worm, best destroyed by violent purging. There is scarcely a society, primitive or otherwise, that has not used this method as a first recourse to treatment, and to see that the concept which gave rise to it was retained in its practice we have only to consider that as recently as 200 years ago the Christian doctrine of prayer and purging was used in cases of insanity or so-called possession. From a modern point of view, there is little difference, other than a cultural one, between the medicine man drawing out intrusive spirits and the priest chasing out devilish influence, where both pontificate on the merits of this particular method. Consequently, emetics, diuretics, laxatives and enemas constitute many of the treatments employed by primitives, several of which still have their place in modern herbals and pharmacopoeias. In South America, Guiana Indians use the familiar ipecacuanha as an emetic. In North America it was the custom of the Chippewa to take an infusion of blue cohosh. As a laxative, cascara has long been known to the North American Indians, and a favourite measure of the Blackfeet was a concoction of the roots of dogbane. Indians of the Pomeroon (in the area now known as Guyana) crushed chillies in water and used the liquid as an enema and the Chippewa steeped the inner bark of the white birch for the same purpose. Indeed, the enema as an artefact has so many ethnic forms, ranging in Africa alone from the simple bamboo tube or hollowed gourd to the more elaborate carved ivory model, that an exhibition of them would make interesting viewing were it not for the sobering nature of their purpose. The seventeenth-century French artist Antoine Watteau has given us what must be the most delicate portrayal of this aspect of getting rid of disease in his engraving of an apothecary's boy, standing fragile-faced yet noble, with his enema syringe held smartly across his right shoulder like a rifle, ready to go forth and do battle against the demons of ill-health.

It is in down-to-earth treatments such as these that, even though his spiritual instruction suggested them, the medicine man is happy to relinquish his authority. The most highly prized of his medicines he retains, passing them down from father to son, but he leaves the business of coping with common complaints to others.

Making the most of raw materials comes naturally to tribal people; their way of life depends on it, and they display an intelligent and imaginative use of plants that most of us would find difficult to equal. South American Indians know at a glance which fibres will make strong ropes, and that if they smear latex on their skin it will suffocate parasites; over a hundred of the plants they use economically have potential value still untapped in the West. The Liberian Mano know that rubbing themselves with red palm oil will protect them from hookworm, and they use over 200 plants for various purposes, many of them medical. Amazonian Indians know where to extract not only medicines but contraceptives and insecticides too. Flowers and leaves are dried and used as decoctions, or mixed with fats to make ointments; roots and barks are inhaled as smoke or steam; stimulants and narcotics are distractions from a humdrum existence. The lists are endless, and discussion of specific plants employed by primitives is more properly postponed until their discovery by adventurers and botanists who made them available to the rest of the world, and the point at which they became part of orthodox medicine.

But what of the medicine man now? That his profession must be one of the oldest alone deserves respect, but the contribution of the wealth of his knowledge to modern pharmacy is a debt that we can only hope to repay by caring for his people where he no longer can.

Carlos Castaneda has a lot to answer for in his reverent gospels on the doings of the Yaqui Indian, Don Juan. What he no doubt intended to be an elaborate portrayal of a typical medicine man immersed in his plant lore in a natural setting, to be viewed with respect as an anthropological wonder and a classic study for posterity, was seen by some critics as the convoluted tale of a thigh-slapping old charlatan, nibbling bits of this and that, materialising and dematerialising in a shimmer of drug-induced states. Our mouths, first opened in wonderment, are contorted into stifled yawns by the third volume.

More important is anthropologist Colin Turnbull's account of the Ik from the mountainous borders of Uganda and Kenya, and their old medicine man, Lolim. For oracle, he used his own sandals, which he would throw on the ground and then pick up like a telephone receiver to listen to ancestral advice, but they were not able to tell him that he would be turned out and abandoned by his tribe because he had no way of providing for them in their starvation. Or perhaps they did, but he simply chose to savour for a little longer the reflections of his former glory before the mutinous glances became too pointed, when he was forced to wander off, without ritual or ceremony, to die alone.

In 1986, it was broadcast that South African medicine men had a cure for AIDS. Experts, of course, remain sceptical, but as in the past we have so often followed his lead it would be nice to hope that the medicine man has again scored another first.

3

The Forming of Order

Jericho, often considered the first town, was founded in Palestine over 10,500 years ago. Around 2,000 years later, the first recognised city, Catal Huyuk, was built in Turkey, but the human race is usually regarded as having moved from prehistoric community to ancient civilisation around 6,000 years ago, a date that coincides with when, for the first time, one generation could give through the written word an account of itself to others that followed.

Writing was a development of the Sumerians, who came from the Persian highlands and settled in the southern part of Mesopotamia between the two rivers Tigris and Euphrates. Their scribes sliced the tips of the river reeds into wedge-shaped styluses and imprinted cruciform marks on to wet clay. We cannot estimate how much of medical history has been lost through not having been recorded, but there are enough references to medicinal plants in the writings of the earliest civilisations to know that their pharmacy had matured beyond its neolithic infancy.

Many of the ancient drugs have familiar associations and we do not have to be scholars of antiquity to be able to give some context to them. For instance, frankincense and myrrh immediately recall the Bible. Opium and ginseng are reminiscent of China. The olive has a special place with the classical Greeks. Iris and horehound are evocative of Horus and Egypt.

The Bible makes a fitting introduction to the medicine of the ancient world, representing in its first scenario the relationship between humankind and the fruits of the earth, and covering in its history all the civilisations to which we will refer.

Olive
Olea europaea
Used for its oil since ancient times

As we may imagine, the pharmacy of the Bible is as rich and varied as the imagery of its tales. Its first image, the allegorical apple, has a modest record as a medicine. Used preventatively it will keep the doctor away, we are told, but it is not much more than a source of vitamin C, a mild laxative and the basis of strong cider. However, the apple is so familar a fruit it is easy to see how it came to be used as a common symbol. In the first place, the apple tree is hardy and adaptable to a great many climates, rather like ourselves. Childhood associations strengthen the bond. The apple tree was there to be climbed. When in flower its scent brings back memories of good days messing about in the garden. Its fruit offers the double temptation, either of tasting too soon, too green and too sour, or, when ripened, to scrump wilfully over someone else's fence. Appropriate punishments are suffered by those rash enough to succumb – chronic indigestion or the shame of being caught.

Still, its involvement in childhood mischief hardly qualifies it for the role it has come to play in the story of our downfall. It is hard to imagine, after all, the harmless apple causing such a sensation so soon after the Creation. It is true that its golden replica did precipitate a great deal of jealousy and subsequent trouble in Greek mythology, when it became the coveted prize to be presented by Paris to the beautiful rivals, Athene, Hera and Aphrodite. Contributed by Eris, goddess of hate, it lived up to its name of the Apple of Discord. Sinister too was the apple offered to Snow White, but only because it had been poisoned. In nature, the apple represents a wholesome thing.

In fact, the unspecified fruit that Eve offered Adam has only been portrayed by artists as the apple. The Bible merely mentions that the fruit grew on the Tree of Knowledge of Good and Evil. Imagine that the fruit was a fig. It seems a more suitable contender: its leaves were apparently at hand, offering a shield for

Fig
Ficus carica
Eve's offering to Adam?

51

newly bashful eyes, and it has significance in other religions. Buddhists believe that one of its species was the tree the Buddha was sitting under at his moment of enlightenment. The Muslims call it the Tree of Heaven. Almost 2,000 years ago, Egyptians recorded its harvesting on a tomb wall. To the Greeks it was the sacred gift of Dionysus and used as a fertility symbol at his festivals. As for its powers of seduction, its dull purple skin is not as inviting as the apple's rosiness, but its luscious fruit is far more exotic and suggestive of temptation than the cool white flesh of the apple.

Wormwood
Artemisia absinthium
The principal ingredient of absinthe. It was used in ancient times to dispel worms.

The legend of wormwood also has a place in the Garden of Eden. When the serpent, still lurking to enjoy the spectacle, was cursed by its creator and sent slithering on its guilty way, from its wavy tracks sprang this bitter herb, principal ingredient of the decadent absinthe, and appropriately used in ancient times to dispel worms. However, in excess, its poison can be as venomous and as treacherous as its mythical origins.

52

Mustard, vinegar, bitter herbs and brimstone; as we can see, the Bible was not all milk and honey, but there was a balm. 'Is there no balm in Gilead?' asked the prophet Jeremiah. 'Is there no physician there? Why then is not the health of the daughter of my people healed?' He directed also, 'Go into Gilead and take balm . . .' Jacob bade his sons return again to the ruler of Egypt with an offering of 'a little balm and a little honey' to sweeten him up. The term 'balm', used figuratively, describes a substance that can assuage physical suffering. The aromatic resin that is described in the Bible as the 'balm of Gilead' seeps from the cracks and fissures commonly formed in the barks of trees of a species of the genus *Commiphora*. It now has little use other than as an incense but, as a bitter, antiseptic medicine, wonderful properties were formerly ascribed to it.

Another species of *Commiphora* gives us myrrh; again fragrant but bitter tasting, with antiseptic properties and once used as a common mouth wash. Its namesake is Myrrha, whom the gods turned into a tree to protect her from her father's wrath after she had tricked him into incest. The tears she wept (from remorse or from the frustration of being turned into a block of wood, we are not told) are said to be the bitter resin that collects in reddish-brown masses on the myrrh tree.

Frankincense comes from the same family as both these other resins, but is less closely related botanically to myrrh than is balm of Gilead. However, in the biblical context it has close associations, in that both frankincense and myrrh were brought with gold to Christ at his birth by the wise men. Symbolically, they still play a healing role in religious ceremonies, their sweet-scented smoke seeming to provide an atmosphere of sensory harmony.

Black hellebore, or the Christmas rose, also has a traditional association with Christmas. According to a medieval tale, it first grew where an angel had touched the ground and conjured a floral gift for an empty-handed child to give the newborn baby. But this dainty story does not reveal the plant's poisonous nature which can cause convulsions and death. It contains a powerful heart stimulant that is no longer used in general medicine, but is referred to by the Greeks and Romans and was used by apothecaries during the Middle Ages and later as a poison, a purgative and a treatment for depressive madness.

The palm and the pomegranate, together with cinnamon and almonds, are others of the forty-odd medicinal sources referred

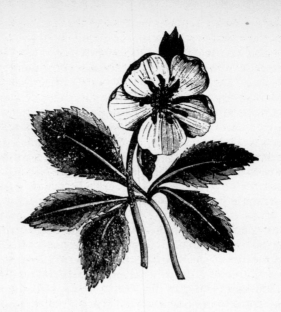

Black Hellebore
Helleborus niger
Also known as the Christmas rose. It first grew, according to a medieval tale, where an angel had touched the ground.

to in the Bible, but while Solomon sang of the 'powders of the merchant' and we may read of the 'many medicines of the Egyptians' or how the Good Samaritan administered oil and wine, our reliance on the information of this text has to be based on faith rather than fact. Of course, there is no reason to doubt that these plants had traditional uses, but it is only when direct evidence is unearthed that we can be certain of positive proof.

When we talk about the ancient world, it is usually with reference to a very small part of the globe – the Middle East and those who invaded it. The Sumerians may have invented writing but, as far as medical history is concerned, the Chinese must claim the first herbal text. It is difficult to pinpoint dates for Shên Nung, as references to his reign range from 'some 2,000 years ago' to 'around 3,000 years BC'. One authority has it that he was in power from 2838–2698 BC, which would have made him a tidy old age even for a venerable Chinese emperor, but by consensus he is believed to have made his mark between 2,700 and 3,000 years ago with the compilation of his *Pen Tsao* or *Great Herbal*. In it he listed 365 medicinal plants and remedies, although this number is often exaggerated up to the thousand mark, including many of those that are still in use today, such as Chinese rhubarb, poppy, cannabis, croton, aconite and ephedra. Probably the most remarkable inclusion was chaulmoogra oil, which remained the most widely used treatment for leprosy in the Eastern world, and was introduced to the West in the middle of the nineteenth century. Its champion in the twentieth century was the botanist and Chinese scholar Dr Joseph Rock, who was commissioned in the 1920s to trace its true source, but we will deal with his adventures and the botany of chaulmoogra later.

Shên Nung. He has been referred to in the West as the Chinese Hippocrates (our 'Father of Medicine') but, as he predates his Greek rival by over 2,000 years, it might be considered more respectful to his memory to call Hippocrates the Greek Shên Nung. We dare not, of course, for fear of causing an uproar, and cries of 'He may only have been a legend!', but, legend or not, some person or persons compiled this ancient pharmacopoeia, which has been so highly esteemed in China that, from the first century AD until the sixteenth century, four different editions were printed. It is still in print, and for this alone deserves a little more than a cursory nod of recognition.

To return to the Sumerians and our own ancient world . . . in their Garden of Eden between the two rivers they prospered. Around the middle of the fourth millennium BC, they looked at the alluvial mud newly raised from the Persian Gulf by the silt of the Tigris and Euphrates, at their own craggy mountain tops and into the distance where they knew lay the arid Arabian desert. Below there flourished towering reeds and date palms; birds flocked; fish teemed in the tributaries; game ran wild. They would have been fools not to have wanted to settle there. Dykes were built, channels cut and swamps drained. The soil was easily watered, and very fertile. Crops yielded nearly a hundred-fold return on their sowing; more than enough for subsistence and plenty to trade. As a rural community they were doing very well indeed; so well, in fact, that they became the first urbanised society. Buttressed temples made of bricks of river mud sprang up like anthills, each supporting a community of servants to the deity it honoured. Taxes were paid into the temple funds by each member of the divine household, and the priests and priestesses were obliged to take slabs of clay and river reeds and present them to newly ordained scribes, bidding them to do the necessary arithmetic. Thus organised accountancy was created and the position of secretary instated. In time all knowledge, whether of the temple's wealth or the natural world, came to be recorded and the language of the people transcribed into the written word.

From this land, aptly said to be the Garden of Eden's secret identity, appropriately came one of the first known herbals. Clay tablets listing 1,000 medicinal plants lay buried for 4,000 years, under the ruins of the city of Nippur. But what has also come to light is that, for all this élite race's astronomical calculations, its art, its mathematics, for all its architecture and its giving the day twenty-four hours, it still believed that to have disease was to be possessed by the supernatural and that the priests and priestesses were the obvious doctors. More than shades of Shamanism here.

The Assyrians and the Babylonians inherited this magico-religious approach to disease and created a few of their own prescriptions to expel demons but, while remaining conceptually at a standstill, medicine began to branch out and to be organised in a professional sense. Herbalism became a specialist practice and although disease was diagnosed by the priest-diviner's consulting an oracle of the entrails of sacrificed animals, during Hammurabi's reign in Babylon around 2000 BC, rules were imposed, intended to protect both patient and doctor. The king had his social ideals engraved on basalt, the Stele of Hammurabi, where he is portrayed receiving a sacred scroll from the sun-god Shamash, and beneath this image is minutely inscribed his divine code of social practice. Doctors were to be paid specific fees, more for masters – less for slaves, and must in turn pay the penalty of their failure to save a patient's life, if not with an arm or a leg, then certainly with a finger or a hand. Leniency was shown if the patient had been only a slave, in which case the physician merely had to remove the corpse and provide a live replacement.

Long before Hippocrates' noble oath to medical ethics, Hammurabi's code of medical practice, if a little shaky democratically, was laying the foundations for the principle that there should be safeguards for both physician and patient. Diagnosis had attained the rather more practical level of being anyone's guess. The sick were left in the market squares, and passers-by were encouraged to offer their several opinions. Prescriptions from medicinal plants and methods of treatment were pre-ordained and to be adhered to. Medicine was slowly moving from magical to empirical lore.

King Ashurbanipal, who reigned in the mid-seventh century BC, studiously collected all manner of written knowledge, and tablets recovered from his library in the ruined Assyrian city of Nineveh listed 300-odd drugs, including the names of trees, herbs, types of seeds, juices and roots. Storax, myrrh and opium provided some sticky ingredients. Particular conditions were allocated specific remedies. Plant enemas and poultices were still popular, due to the continuing belief that treating the sick was on a par with exorcising the possessed, but practical measures were also advised: rest and quiet, massage and attention to diet. Symptoms were described and the life centre was said to be situated in the liver.

While Mesopotamian medicine was accumulating the knowledge of passing civilisations, slab on slab, the Egyptians were not idling in this field. As early as 2500 BC they were busying themselves with ink and papyrus, inaugurating a class of literati, the new professionals, who included architects, engineers and physicians as distinct from priests. Imhotep had set the pace at around 2900 BC by including all aspects of these fields among his legendary talents. He designed for his king, Zoser, a stepped pyramid incorporating stone in its construction, and became the first named architect. He was given the honour of becoming court physician and later was elevated, as a paragon of wisdom in many spheres, to the rank of deity, patron of medicine. Between ancient civilisations, gods tended to be inherited, and he later became identified with Asclepius, the Greek god of medicine. Pyramids blistered across the deserts. Slaves were given garlic and onions to prevent infections as they laboured in the merciless heat to construct these skyward-pointing launching pads to the celestial kingdoms.

In the cool and dark interiors of tombs, dates were stored, pressed figs and beeswax, ointments and flower oils were stockpiled as provisions against the needs of the journey from mortality. To arrive looking decent, self-respecting Egyptian queens took their cosmetics with them: kohl made from the black metallic powder antimony and henna (sometimes known as Egyptian privet), to dye the hair and decorate the skin, made from the powdered leaves of a shrub much admired by Egyptian ladies for its thick and fragrant panicles of red flowers. Drugs were stored in decorated boxes and alabaster pots. Perfumes were oil or wine based. The sacred embalming perfume, Kyphi, included myrrh, cinnamon, juniper, honey and raisins steeped in wine. It seems that a great deal of pharmaceutical activity was being spent on the well-being of corpses, and nothing demonstrates this irony better than the practice of mummifying.

In the fifth century BC, the Greek historian Herodotus recorded some methods employed for this. Brain and intestines were removed, and the intestinal cavity cleansed with palm wine. The hollow parts were then filled with ground aromatics and an assortment of spices, left for a little over two months and then wrapped with gummed bandages. A cheaper method was to introduce cedar oil into the body, stopper it up and leave it to dissolve the inner organs, whereupon it was released, leaving only skin and bones. Shortcuts were taken for the poor. Herodotus did not mention what became of the inner organs but we now know that these were cleansed and put in a pickling solution, set aside with the body, then retrieved, sprinkled with the sawdust of fragrant barks, fashioned into an approximate original shape and wrapped tightly in linen bandages, either to be stored in jars or laid with their owners.

It was from between the knees of a mummy at Thebes that the Ebers Papyrus was retrieved, according to the Arab who sold this seventy-odd-feet long medical scroll to George Ebers in the early 1870s. It was dated from about 1500 BC and lists over 850 prescriptions and remedies. The emphasis was definitely on herbalism. The Edwin Smith Papyrus dated a little earlier and, dealing with surgery and setting fractures, ran to only fifteen feet. The Egyptians, for all their practice on corpses, were loth, for religious reasons, to tamper with live bodies. The embalmers in any case were an inferior and separate order to the physicians.

While in 1500 BC the Indians were composing their sacred medical poem the *Rig Veda*, one of the earliest Sanskrit writings, the Egyptians were jotting down all they knew on their papyrus, which was made from the pith of the stems of the tall marsh plant *Cyperus papyrus*. Spells and incantations still accompanied treatment, allowing for haphazard variation and admitting the usual element of superstition, but prescriptions were specific and strictly adhered to. Order was being enforced, which was good. Inspired or experimental medicine was severely restricted, bringing progress to a halt, which was bad. The physician was considered free from blame if a patient died, so long as prescribed treatment had been followed. If not, and the physician lost a patient's life, he forfeited his own. Nevertheless, although surgery was limited, they knew that the heart played a more vital role than the liver. Diagnosis often resorted to astrology, but not always; doctrines of a healthy diet and cleanliness were observed. Herodotus records that the Egyptians were particular about purging themselves regularly, stemming from the more rational belief that diseases were due to the impurity of their food rather than possession by demons. Physicians, and the few surgeons that existed, trained at medical schools. By the time of Cleopatra, who was herself apparently no novice in medical matters for she is alleged to have written several works on gynaecological problems and venereal disease, pharmacological experimentation, albeit on poisons, was being practised, and slaves were used as guinea pigs to test the potency of asp venom. Many of the vegetable drugs that the Egyptians used then, such as opium, saffron, castor and olive oil, are still in use today.

Castor Oil Plant
Ricinis communis
One of the many vegetable drugs of the Egyptians

Within its limits, Egyptian medicine went as far towards the rational as was possible, but by the fourth century BC it could go no farther alone, and deteriorated into what has been described as 'a miserable sort of alchemy and magic'. Like his Egyptian predecessor, the persona of the Greek god Asclepius may have been based on an ordinary mortal. Historically, he is believed to have lived around 1200 BC, been father to two military surgeons and famed for his miraculous cures. In mythology, he was the son of Apollo, and one of his symbols was the serpent, which stood for renovation and was believed to have had powers of un-earthing medicinal herbs. He was first worshipped in Athens in 420 BC and, before this date, temples of healing were erected at Epidaurus and Cos in his honour. These were resorts for the sick who made pilgrimages to them, stopping overnight in the hope that redemption from their ills would come to them in dreams. According to records from the temple at Epidaurus, this usually happened, and there may have been some truth in the claim. While we may be sceptical of miracle cures, there is certainly something to be said for a change of environment and the placebo effect. For example, in the Middle Ages, those unfortunates who were stricken with the mysterious St Anthony's Fire often as a last resort made a pilgrimage to St Anthony's shrine and, as a consequence, were often cured. Miraculously, they thought. What had actually happened was that they had, by setting off on their pilgrimage, left the environment that was producing rye infected with the fungus ergot, of which lysergic acid is a derivative, and so discontinued slowly poisoning themselves.

That the Greeks' temple retreats were beneficial health-wise, there can be no doubt. Strict cleanliness was observed. Healthy exercise and diet were doctor's orders and, above all, the physician–priests of these establishments cared. They were referred to as Asclepiads and it was in the region of one of their major temples, on the island of Cos, that the Father of Medicine, Hippocrates, was born.

Again, there is dispute as to the actual identity of Hippocrates. He did exist, but may not have been the sole author of many of the writings attributed to him. Nevertheless, whether the words of wisdom he spoke were entirely his own views or laced with the doctrines of many, they were based on the observation of facts rather than belief in fictions, and they allowed medicine to develop from a superstition into a science: 'To know is one thing, merely to believe one knows is another. To know is science, but merely to believe one knows is ignorance.'

Hippocrates adhered to the principle that there is no authority except facts; that facts are obtained by accurate observation and that deductions are to be made only from facts. Yet he recognised difficulties in discovering these: 'Life is short and the art [of medicine] is long, the occasion fleeting, experience fallacious and judgement difficult.' He did not advocate the plethora of drugs that the Egyptians used magically; he was done with magic, and more concerned with environmental treatment.

His diagnoses were in accord with the current belief (which he presumably took to be fact!) that the four elements – fire, air, earth and water – were reflected in the four humours of the body – blood, phlegm, yellow bile and black bile – and that good health depended on a harmonious balance between them. We know that there is rather more to the body's elements than these, but he wasn't so far off the mark. He considered disease to be not simply 'one big ill', but the result of many causes. He knew that a consumptive patient with a racking cough, pale, hollow cheeks lit with an unhealthy flush, was not in immediate danger of

Hippocrates
Popularly known as the father of medicine

dying, and that a slow death could be interrupted by sunshine and rest in the mountains. He also knew that a patient with a high fever, chest pains and delirium would die soon and suddenly, or as suddenly recover, and that meanwhile treatment need be no other than fresh air, bed rest and a liquid diet. Such a rational approach was not seen again for 1,800 years. He had little patience with unfounded views, such as epilepsy being a sacred disease, or that it could be contracted by eating goat flesh or lying on goat skins, and argued that it was no more sacred than any other disease, also pointing out that those who kept goats as a living were no more likely to suffer from epilepsy than anyone else.

Basically he believed, or observed, that in many cases the body heals itself, and that our attitudes to ill-health go a long way to correcting it: 'Our natures are the physicians of our diseases.' And, of course, he founded the Hippocratic Oath, which incorporates the declaration: '. . . I will give no deadly drug to any, though it be asked of me, nor will I counsel such . . .' Those drugs he did prescribe were yet again largely purgatives and emetics – black and white hellebore, for instance – but the number included in the Hippocratic collection amounted to more than 300. As testament to his teachings, he lived to be over eighty. Before he died, Aristotle was born.

Aristotle's father was a physician to King Amyntas II, grandfather of Alexander the Great, and he followed in his father's footsteps by becoming the shining light of ancient biological knowledge, and later tutor to the young Alexander. He studied under Plato at the Athenian Academy, and seems to have been a favourite pupil. Plato called him 'the mind of the school', and he in turn remained there faithfully, first as student and then lecturer, until Plato's death in 347 BC. Then, with four fellow students, Xenocrates, Erastus, Coriscus and Theophrastus, he opened up a school in the city and seaport of Assos. Three years later, probably at the suggestion of his friend Theophrastus, he settled for a while in Lesbos (Theophrastus' birthplace) and, putting aside philosophy for a while, took to studying marine biology and natural history.

Aristotle, like Hippocrates, was concerned with observing biological facts, although much of what he wrote seems still to have been based on hearsay and common beliefs. For instance, he had some unsubstantiated notions about the infertility of men under the age of twenty-one (surely there was enough empirical evidence around to disprove this? Or were all the young men too

Theophrastus
Regarded as having founded the science of botany

rapt in thought or with one another?) and that excessive menstruation was a symptom of excessive desire. However, he knew
that semen was the same colour, whatever the colour of the
owner's skin, and took Herodotus to task for writing otherwise.

His friend and colleague, Theophrastus, is of particular interest
to the history of pharmacy. He succeeded Aristotle as head of
their Lyceum, and founded the science of botany. As one of the
'new sceptics', he observed the action of plants on the body, as
opposed to simply believing in their powers. He contemptuously
described the traditional methods of collecting medicinal plants,
scorning, for instance, the belief that the hellebore should be cut
standing towards the east while saying prayers, and that caution
should be taken that no eagle was in sight, for it was an omen of
death within the year. The woodpecker was a danger too; if it
caught sight of a peony being dug up in the middle of the night,
the culprit would surely lose his sight. Lucky for some that
woodpeckers are not nocturnal and that there is little fun to be had
in midnight peony cropping. He quoted mockingly on the
venerated gathering of mandrake:

> It is said that one should draw three circles round mandrake
> with a sword and cut it with one's face towards the west; and
> at the cutting of the second piece one should dance round the
> plant and say as many things as possible about the mysteries
> of love . . .

Mandrake
Mandragora officinarum
Considered in the Middle Ages to have powerful magical properties

Mandrake was nevertheless regarded up to and beyond the Middle Ages as powerful magic, its roots being reminiscent of the human form and said to scream when pulled up. The fatal dangers of doing this were averted from the human collector by tying a dog to the plant and allowing the poor creature to do the dirty work. In the Middle Ages it was believed to be seeded by the sperm of hanged men and to grow under gallows; witches smeared its juice on their bodies prior to taking off on their broomsticks. For centuries it was regarded as a powerful aphrodisiac, and the Romans in particular enjoyed its effects at their orgies. It has been portrayed variously, from engravings on Egyptian tombs and Assyrian temples to seventeenth-century woodcuts, and its many so-called attributes have been described in texts ranging from the Bible to Anglo-Saxon herbals. It is true, however, that it is powerful stuff. Native to the Mediterranean and Europe, its far-reaching roots have been used as anaesthetic, poison and panacea. It contains atropine, an alkaloid which in small doses will excite the heartbeat but in large doses will paralyse all the muscles, including the heart.

Before his death in 285 BC, Theophrastus wrote a number of

manuscripts dealing with plants, but his *Historia Plantarum* has remained the most famous. Partly drawn from personal observations, partly from hearsay, it dealt with the collection and preparation of vegetable drugs, with perfumes, spices and plant diseases, and was a standard textbook of its type for 2,000 years, earning for his memory the title of Father of Botany.

In 323 BC, aged thirty-two and at the height of his youthful glory, Alexander the Great died of a fever in Babylon, within a year of his former teacher, Aristotle. He left no successor, and his realms were split among his generals. With the decline of Greece came the rise of Rome. Many of the Greek physicians migrated to Rome and to parts of her empire but, as a conquered race, their place in society was subordinate. Rome, in any case, did not have much time for doctoring, which was split in its society among herb gatherers, drug pedlars, slaves and a few wise women. Medicine was not a respectable profession, and beneath the dignity of most Roman nobles. Whereas the Greeks were the classic thinkers and theorists, primarily teachers, the Romans were the classic doers. Their interests were more in military matters than philosophy or medicine, and white cabbage steeped in wine did for a multitude of complaints. But they started to take notice of the Greek element, and their energetic engineering feats, sophisticated sanitary conditions and love of bathing would have reinforced and complemented Hippocrates' own views on the rudiments of health. Unfortunately, Hippocrates was no longer around, and much of his practical approach was corrupted by his Greek followers, who were to an extent resorting to the sort of complicated formulary that he had denounced. Nevertheless, in 46 BC, when Julius Caesar awarded Greek physicians the right to citizenship, their status was promoted, and those that had been trained in the major Greek medical schools and at the great medical school of Alexandria (founded a year before Alexander's death) were treated with respect. By the turn of the century, young Roman citizens themselves were considering careers of healing rather than battling, although Romanised Greeks still very much dominated the profession.

Aulus Cornelius Celsus lived in the first century AD and wrote one of the first great medical works to come from Rome. His *De Medicina* listed at least 250 drugs and mentioned a hundred surgical instruments, but it was largely ignored by his contemporaries, only finding fame nearly 1,500 years later, after it was published in 1478.

Pliny (born AD 23) followed with his eight books on medical botany, from among an impressive thirty-seven volumes on art, science and natural history, *Historia Naturalis*. He was not a physician but an encyclopaedist and, although considered the wisest man of his time, what he wrote was an uncritical compilation of the work of over a hundred personally selected authors. Scribonius Largus (*circa* AD 43) was a physician in the Roman army and is famed for his handbook on the military expedition to Britain, *De Compositione Medicamentorum*, and for introducing opium and ginger to this island. However, the star of the Roman show has to be Dioscorides.

Pedianos Dioscorides wrote at the age of about twenty-seven (in AD 77) the famous *De Materia Medica*, which in later years qualified him to become another of the 'Fathers', this time of pharmacognosy – and justifiably so, as this was to become the standard textbook of its type for 1,500 years. Legend has it that he was physician to Antony and Cleopatra; historically it is known that he served for a time as surgeon in Nero's army, and probably his extensive travels in this capacity enabled him to collect much of the material for this incredibly comprehensive treatise on the properties and uses of medicinal plants. Not only did it refer to about 600 plants, but also methods of cultivation, collection, storage and selection. We know today that there is indeed 'a time to reap', and that the poppy's morning yield of morphine is four times greater than in the evening, and that flowering often coincides with an increase of a plant's active principle. Dioscorides in his day was aware of these things; he also advised that the juice of herbs should be taken from newly sprouted shoots and roots should be gathered when the plant's leaves were falling. He referred to a 'better quality of drug' and was concerned with standards of ingredients; for instance, ginger that had not started to mould, olive oil that was oldest and fattiest and cardamoms that were difficult to break open and not quite ripe.

As regards the storage of drugs, he suggested that:

Flowers and sweet-scented things should be laid up in dry boxes of limewood: but there are some herbs which do well enough if wrapped up in papers or leaves for the preservation of their seeds. For moist medicines some thicker material such as silver, or glass, or horn will agree best. Yes, and earthenware if it be not thin is fitting enough, and so is wood, particularly if it be box-wood. Vessels of brass will be suitable for eye medicines and for liquids and for all that are compounded of vinegar or of liquid pitch or of Cedria, but fats and marrows ought to be put in vessels of tin.

He prescribed several remedies for an affliction which apparently concerned men then as much as it does now. To them it was 'fox mange'; we call it baldness, and as hair restorers he recommended, among other things, the rather unlikely radish, hazelnuts, or the inner skin of walnut shells, burnt and mixed with oil. Tapeworms, he said, could be 'shaken out and killed' by a decoction of pomegranate roots, 'expelled' with mulberry root or 'drawn out' with garlic. Cancerous tumours, he said, could be helped by the root bark of the oak or dissolved with cabbage, crocus, squirting cucumber or vetch, and there is current evidence that claims for the latter two were not without foundation. As a means of contraception, juniper berries used internally prevented conception, as did the taking of white poplar bark mixed with mule's kidney. Here the white poplar bark seems to be erroneous, but the use of juniper berries and mule's kidney can be to an extent substantiated by the former's action as a uterine stimulant and the latter's relationship to horse's urine which, in common with the modern pill, contains oestrogen.

Needless to say, these few and very incomplete examples of Dioscorides' knowledge do not by any means describe its full extent, but they do give an indication of it. Of particular interest is his anticipation of a drug with which we are all very familiar – aspirin. He held that a decoction of the leaves of the white willow was '. . . an excellent fomentation for ye gout . . .' and this was used for centuries as a traditional remedy for all manner of painful problems, including headache, toothache and earache. The only drawback with this remedy was that it could not be taken internally and had to be applied externally. In 1827, however, a French chemist isolated from a common feathery-flowered herb, meadowsweet, known then as *Spiraea ulmaria* (now *Filipendula ulmaria*) an ingredient which was soon found to be contained in the juice and bark of several willows. He called it salicin after *Salix*, the Latin name for willow. Ten years later a derivative of this, salicylic acid, was discovered, but both these were still only suitable for external application. At the end of the nineteenth century, the Germans made the big breakthrough with the preparation of acetylsalicylic acid, which they named aspirin in commemoration of the original *Spiraea*. It was, of course, a great success, and a considerable improvement on nature which, unfortunately, is never quite perfect. She caters for too many dependants to be able singularly to serve one species; it is left to us to refine or synthesise her disordered bounties into such indispensable remedies as the white crystalline powder of aspirin.

A particularly useful feature of *De Materia Medica* was that it contained nearly 400 coloured illustrations. Their accuracy was not, however, above criticism; as Dioscorides' contemporary Pliny pointed out of plants, they '. . . change and alter their form every quarter of a year'. The pictures were probably based on the botanic illustrations of Krateus, physician to King Mithridates of Pontus, in the century before. Still, in retrospect, one is reluctant to focus on the faults of Dioscorides because his monumental achievement has stood the test of time so well and is referred to even now. Galen, who followed, for all his stardom in the history of medicine, never shone with half such brilliance.

Galen was another Greek, born in AD 130 at Pergamum, where at the age of fourteen his father, an architect, had him educated by the best teachers, from whom he learnt all the works of the classic philosophers, mathematicians and logicians. When Galen was seventeen his father 'had a dream', and decided that his son was destined for medicine, which for the next ten years he studied at the major medical schools, including the most famous at Alexandria. After graduating, he became physician to the gladiators in Pergamum but after four years, finding this rather too distasteful and not in keeping with his academic qualifications, he settled in Rome and became a member of the high society, which seemed to have welcomed him with open arms. Colleagues in the medical profession disliked him intensely. He was successful, conceited and highly critical of others' practices – not without justification – but these were not endearing qualities, and he was forced to return to his home town.

Shortly after arriving at Pergamum he was recalled to Rome by the joint emperors Marcus and Lucius (adoptive brothers), legendarily to cure the former of a stomach ache (which he apparently managed to do), historically to accompany them on their conquering expeditions. He made his excuses and was left in Rome to look after the health of the heir-apparent. He wrote, lectured, and opened up a drug shop. He remained an active physician, but an egotistical one. He revived the works of Hippocrates, to his credit, but he did not have his predecessor's genius, clarity of thought or intellectual honesty. He believed that he knew – and we may recall what Hippocrates said of this. Galen too adopted the principle that health depended on a harmonious balance between the four humours of the body, but instead of adhering to the practical treatments that Hippocrates had advised, he incorporated the use of a multitude of drugs – often as many as a hundred in a single prescription – and when patients recovered (as patients often do, regardless of treatment) he claimed full credit for the cure. All his medicines' ingredients he gauged by degree in relationship to their effect on the humours. For instance, pepper was a fourth-degree heater, whereas cucumber was a fourth-degree cooler; the expression 'cool as a cucumber' is reminiscent of his theories.

Unfortunately, Galen's theories became dogmas, and ones which were followed for the next 1,300 years, until what remained of his writings were publicly burnt by the rumbustious and equally conceited Paracelsus. This, incidentally, was ironic, perhaps even symbolic, since in Galen's own lifetime the majority of his work, which is estimated to have been in the region of 500 manuscripts, was destroyed in a fire at his home in Rome. This tragedy he did not deserve. Nor, perhaps, does he deserve all the criticism that is levelled against him; indeed, his work in the field of experimental anatomy and physiology is to be commended – and usually is, by anatomists and physiologists. He would probably have been rewarded with acclaim in all spheres had his dogmatic arrogance not been so hard to swallow. He said, patronisingly, of his better, Hippocrates: 'He opened the road; I have made it passable.' Certainly he would have enjoyed this as a fitting epitaph. However, the remark made twelve centuries later by Henri de Mandeville, lecturer in anatomy at the medical school of Montpellier, seems more apt: 'God did not exhaust all His creative powers in making Galen.'

At least in his lifetime, while Galen held the reins, Roman medicine was going some way in the right direction. After his death, the reins were in anybody's hands. Physicians became more ignorant, more dogmatic and, as the Roman Empire declined, the preparation of medicines fell to magicians, poisoners and prostitutes. To an extent, the environment remained well cared for and even improved. Some 300 million gallons of clean drinking water were daily supplied to Rome via fourteen magnificent aqueducts, piped into the homes of the wealthy and collected from public fountains by the less fortunate. Flush lavatories were common; bathing was popular. Hospitals were well equipped and efficiently run, although these were primarily for the wealthy, or for soldiers. Despite these advances, however, disease played an important part in Rome's downfall. Where the Romans had once been the conquerors, others were now doing the conquering and much of the sanitary engineering and water supplies were destroyed. Malaria took hold and conditions allowed for the spread of many of the diseases inherited from the conquered territories. By the latter half of the fifth century, the western part of the Roman Empire had fallen.

The Christian religion, which the Romans had adopted, survived. To their credit, the early Christians maintained the spirit of the Good Samaritan and cared for the sick and needy. To their discredit they staunchly adhered to the alleged word of God: 'I kill and I make alive; I wound and I heal . . .' Healing was in the hands of the Almighty. Healing by mortal men was out. Prayer and penance were in.

Rational medicine came to a standstill altogether in Europe. The few hospitals that did exist were often overcrowded and dirty and had nothing in common with the cleanliness and harmonious atmosphere of the pagan hospitals of the Greeks.

Monkshood
Aconitum napellus
Also known as wolfsbane. All parts of the plant are poisonous but it is used in minute doses in homeopathic medicine and sometimes externally in the form of a liniment for sprains.

Disease was almost welcomed as a means of purifying the soul. Instead of astrological signs influencing different parts of the body and various diseases (a belief prevalent among civilisations that had gone before and one that was revived later), saints were designated to these roles and were prayed to accordingly. Shades of Shamanism once more. Already, at the end of the fourth century, a group of Christian fanatics had burned the medical school at Alexandria to the ground, destroying the 700,000 books in the library. The Greeks, Romans and Egyptians had a cosmopolitan collection of gods which they had borrowed and copied from one another, but none of them was as dogmatic and unswerving in their beliefs as the Christians, with their blind faith in the omnipotence of their single one. Barber-surgeons performed operations and physician-monks preached repentance and purging. There was always purging.

All ancient medical knowledge was not lost, however, and much of it was secreted away safely behind monastic walls. If the monks did not actually act on the wisdom of these classic works, they at least safeguarded them. Meanwhile, the Chinese were busy updating Shên Nung's *Great Herbal* and an eighteen-volume book of medicine, *Nei Ching* (attributed to Emperor Huang), practising acupuncture and balancing their own harmony between the male and female principles Yang and Yin. In India Susruta (fifth century AD), one of the most famous of the Hindu physicians, compiled a manuscript listing more than 750 medicinal plants and the Hindus were balancing their harmony between the three elements: spirit-air, phlegm and bile.

As far as the perpetuation of medical knowledge in the West was concerned, we have the Arabs to thank. From the fourth century AD, theirs was the newly advancing civilisation, and they continued what the Egyptians, Greeks and Romans had started, drawing directly from these ancient sources, thus keeping the scientific spirit alive. A hospital and university was founded in Baghdad, where students studied and translated the works of the Greeks and Romans. Their empire extended almost to the borders of India and nearly to China, and thus the revival of the old learning was augmented by an accumulation of their own. Of course, those names that feature from the Arabian culture do not necessarily have claim to that nationality. The Arabian Empire incorporated many nations, and the fact that the renowned medical school at Salerno, near Naples, was legendarily founded by Adale the Arab, Salernus the Latin, Pontus the Greek and

Elinus the Jew reflects the cosmopolitan nature of their culture.

Rhazes was a medical hero in the mould of Hippocrates. He did not begin his career as a physician (he was first a musician and philosopher) but, on witnessing the appalling conditions in the sick houses of Baghdad, medicine became his motivating interest. He chose a site for a new hospital in the city by hanging pieces of meat at intervals in each area, and had the building built where they putrified slowest. The Father of Medicine would have been pleased. He appropriately became physician-in-charge of this hospital, and wrote prolifically, producing, by the end of his life in AD 932, a voluminous encyclopaedic work on medicine weighing twenty-two pounds and derived from the best of the Greek, Syrian, Arab, Persian and Indian sources.

Avicenna, born half a century later, was a child prodigy and already a court physician at the age of eighteen. He wrote on music, drama, mathematics and alchemy (this was the age of alchemy) but most importantly he left for posterity his great *Canon of Medicine* which remained a standard work until the mid-sixteenth century.

Towards the end of the ninth century in Britain, Alfred of Wessex, aptly named the Great for his wisdom and inventiveness and reverent interest in the natural world, was concerned at the ignorance of his people and their clergy. After ousting from these shores the remaining Vikings (whose berserk marauding was apparently due to a surfeit of hallucinogenic mushrooms!), he established a Court School and invited teachers from abroad to teach there. He sent for medical writings from the East, and had these combined with the traditional folklore of his own land. After his death, *The Leech Book of Bald* was published, Bald reputedly having been a friend of the king's. This text was partly rational, partly superstitious. On the one hand, it held standards for the choosing of drugs: scammony root was to be broken in two, put on the tongue, and if it '. . . bursteth out, as white as milk, the prescribed dose should be only one penny weight'. If the quality was less good, the dosage should be one and a half penny weight. Poor quality was three and no more than that. On the other hand, all piercing pains such as lumbago, sciatica and headaches were said to be the shot of elves. Reflections of Intrusion.

At the turn of the millennium, all was disorder in Europe. Powers struggled for supremacy, populations were undernourished. Life was short and brutish, infant mortality was high.

Scammony
Convolvulus scammonia
This was referred to in the Leech Book of Bald. *The root-resin was used as an efficacious and strong purgative.*

The Christian Church was in a shambles, Popes took mistresses – at least more conspicuously than before – and came and went as fleetingly as under three weeks. In Islam at the end of the eleventh century, the Shi'ite 'assassins', supposedly under the influence of hashish (cannabis), were exerting their heavy-handed political technique which also took its name from them. It was at the end of the eleventh century too that the Crusades began.

This was the time when the medical school at Salerno, now established for nearly 500 years, reached its peak. The Crusaders, returning from their wars, found this Italian port a convenient haven. Many stayed to study there, and not only contributed their own material learned from the Arabs, but took back into Europe all that they had learnt at the medical school, thus promoting its reputation. It became a centre of medical learning and produced at least a hundred medical texts by over thirty authors; it is believed that the first European text on drugs, the *Antidotarium Nicolai* was compiled there.

Due to their varied ancestry, the teachings at Salerno were widely comprehensive but not always disciplined by a strict adherence to science. This is seen in the person of a former student, Michael Scott, who came to play a Merlin role at the court of the German Emperor Frederick II in his capacities as alchemist, astrologer, mathematician and wizard. He is commonly credited with having had a part in relieving the suffering of surgery, by preparing an anaesthetic of henbane, opium and mandrake which was inhaled from a rag soaked in this lethal brew. After this, he claimed, anything could be done to the patient.

The Emperor Frederick himself was, rather as Alfred had been, keenly interested in science. He was, in fact, keenly interested in everything, and lavishly entertained all the most stimulating company he could find, which ranged from philosophers to pretty girls. He looked for answers to all the questions teeming in his active mind. Why did a stick appear to bend in water? How do we know that our soul will last for ever any more than the world itself? He took two prisoners, gave them a good meal, sent one off on a long chase and the other to bed. He then cut them open to see which one had digested his meal the better and found that it was the latter. It was an inspired physiological experiment but cruel, and it must be hoped that they were provided with Michael Scott's anaesthetic. He wrote a beautifully illustrated manual on falconry, *On the Art of Hunting with Birds*, wrote love songs and worried about his spelling. In 1224 he decreed that nobody was

Henbane
Hyoscyamus niger
One of the ingredients in Michael Scott's crude anaesthetic

allowed to call himself a doctor unless this status had been officially approved by examiners, after which a licence would be granted. He also produced a proper curriculum at Salerno, where in 1240 he ordered that medical and pharmaceutical practices were from then on to be two separate professions. Those in the latter were further ordered to mix their drugs according to law.

As Naples was invaded and Salerno's medical school gradually declined, others which had formed during Salerno's greatness continued to flourish. Padua, Bologna, Paris and particularly Montpellier were all notable medical centres. Roger Bacon was an English Franciscan friar who had a great deal of influence in the school at Paris. He was a free thinker, and considered by the Church to be dangerously sacrilegious because of his scientific leanings. He took the view that theories should be upheld by practice, and predicted the coming of mechanical vehicles and a race of super scientists. Bacon was leading in the right direction, and individual members of the clergy were themselves becoming interested in the disciplined teachings of the medical schools.

But in the mid-1300s, progress as well as everything else was halted by the devastation of the plague. The Black Death was brought to Europe by a small fleet of Genoese ships returning from ports on the Black Sea. They struggled as far as Messina in Italy and could go no farther, the ships manned only by the dying. The authorities were shocked by this sight – and frightened. The fleet was immediately ordered out of port, but it was too late and the Messinians did not flee in time. They brought the scourge to Europe, and the following year in 1378 it had reached Britain. Nothing was to be done except wait for it to subside. Physicians ventured out into the streets only with the precaution of ridiculous leather hoods pulled down to their shoulders, which had, projecting from the face, a beak-shaped cone stuffed with aromatics and herbs. The clergy died martyrs to their Christian ethics of looking after the sick, but they had only prayers to offer, no effective medicines or treatment and could only prescribe repentance. This latest invader finally retreated, but it took with it between a third and a half of Europe's population. Those that remained not only profited with their lives but also all that was left behind to share.

Europe staggered to her feet, trade started up again and merchants began to prosper. Guilds were formed. In England the Fraternity of St Anthony, which represented the joint interests of the trades of the pepperers and spicers–apothecaries, demanded that standards should be enforced on the drugs that were sold. This was not only to protect its members' financial interests, but also their reputations against the complaints of fraudulent practices.

They had been accused of mixing roots with herbs, pepper with cumin, cloves with cardamoms, sugar with liquorice and more besides. In 1393 the Fraternity, which had by then formed itself into the Company of Grocers, suggested that persons of its choice should be elected to clean and inspect all crude drugs that came on the market, and these were to be weighed only after they had been approved. The people appointed to do this were called Garblers. This suggestion was accepted and the Company eventually won the exclusive rights to garble (sift and select) all drugs, spices and other imported goods.

In 1478 Celsus' *De Medicina* reappeared and was acknowledged as the first authoritative book on general medicine. As the century drew to a close, the *Ricettario Fiorentino* was compiled at the College of the Art of Medicine in Florence. This was the first official European pharmacopoeia intended as such. Order could finally be seen to be forming.

Clove
Syzygium aromaticum
One of the commodities ordered to be 'garbled' by the Company of Grocers

4

The New Learning

Although in the fifteenth and sixteenth centuries political chaos rampaged across Europe, Italy was a flourishing commercial centre. As the two centuries merged, the Italian merchants prospered by trading in the luxuries that helped disperse the gloom of the Middle Ages and they attained the glamorous social status of being known for having become rich on riches. They wanted their portraits painted, their families immortalised, their houses decorated with frescos. They could afford to be patrons of the arts and, on the profits from trade in silks and spices, which was heightened by Italy's easier access to the East, art could be bought. To the swish of a thousand brushes, Europe painted herself a bright new face which beamed expansively with the joy of enlightenment. The atmosphere that prevailed can only be called a reaction to the shackles of the Middle Ages. The freed spirit was exalted, authority was questioned and a return was made to some serious thinking.

The Renaissance came with the rediscovery of Greek art, which enchanted the Italians, and the Greek philosophers, whom they put on pedestals. As the demand for silks and spices increased, so did the competition to be the first to supply them. The Renaissance map is crazed with new trade routes. Christopher Columbus, for the Spaniards, wanted to prove that the world was round, but he set sail also to find a new way to Indian spices. Vasco da Gama doubled round the Cape of Good Hope and, finding a convenient back door to India, returned with enough spices from Calicut to have considerably panicked the merchants of Venice. 'Spices' then meant more than the aromatic culinary ingredients they imply today. Hemp, sandalwood and opium were spices. Cardamom, nutmeg and cinnamon were spices. What they had in common was that they were all used as medicines. There was then, as there is now, a demand for new medicines and the spice trade was, in reality, primarily the drug trade.

Originally, in the thirteenth century, the merchants who traded in these things were called pepperers and spicers. In the mid-thirteenth century in France, the term apothecary came to be applied to the spicers, indicating their speciality in selling and preparing medicines. The pepperers were, broadly speaking, the more general wholesale traders who positioned themselves near the ports, while the apothecaries opened establishments in the inland cities.

Rather sooner than he had expected, Columbus sailed along the shores of what he imagined was India and landed in the West Indies. He had bridged the unknown expanse between Europe and America but, in so doing, he also broke down the barrier between the diseases of the two continents. Measles, meningitis, diphtheria and smallpox sailed into the West Indies with the Spaniards in 1492. Ten years later, the Portuguese took smallpox to Brazil. Rumours of gold brought Spanish fleets across the ocean with instructions to trade, and every intention of exploiting where they could. In the 1520s and 1530s, the *conquistadores*, first led by Cortés and then by Pizarro, spread smallpox to

Pizarro's landing on the coast of Peru

78

Mexico and Peru while taking the Aztec and Inca kingdoms. They found their gold and new spices, coca and cocoa – both potential corrupters – and brought back syphilis – a certain one.

As the Aztecs' 'flesh of the gods' was psilocybe mushrooms, so was cocoa 'food of the gods'. This is how Linnaeus described the genus of *Theobroma cacao* – the anglicised specific name was adopted because of a confusion between it and the coconut. The Aztec custom was to drink cocoa as a tea made from the beans mixed with capsicum peppers. Cortés may not have enjoyed the initial bitterness of this drink, offered to him by the unfortunate King Montezuma, but later the Spaniards copied the more palatable method of flavouring it with the seed pods of a native orchid which we know as vanilla. Cocoa beans were considered to be of great value, were used in bartering, and taxes were paid into chests full of them. Like our other familiar beverages, coffee and tea, cocoa contains the mild stimulant caffeine.

Rather more stimulating were the coca leaves the Incas chewed (13 million pounds are still chewed yearly by their descendants), although the custom predated their civilisation by at least 1,000 years – a fact revealed by the more recent discovery of the Paracas textile. This superbly designed and coloured cloth was found wrapped around the mummified body of a Peruvian ruler, probably from the Nazca period (AD 500). The head was adorned

Cocoa
Theobroma cacao
The 'food of the gods' of the Aztecs

with gold ornaments, in readiness, Egyptian-style, for the earthly departure, and beneath the body had been buried an urn, containing sustenance for the journey – a few ears of corn and a number of small bags of coca leaves. The coca-chewing habits of the later Incas are well recorded. They kept track of their history by tying knots in lengths of string, using these to reel off verbally the events of the past, which were amply punctuated with coca customs. The son of one of Pizarro's officers, Garcilasso de la Vega, whose mother was a member of the Inca royal family, had inherited from her his own coca plantation, and he recorded in writing what he heard.

Apparently, coca plantations were traditionally established in the lands belonging to the Sun – the royal estates. These plantations were often cultivated by slave or convict labour, as one of the original habitats of the plant was the hot and humid forest regions which made farming punishing work. Like cocoa beans, coca leaves were used for barter. They were used for estimating wealth and thus the habit of chewing them was discouraged among the common people. The common people, however, enjoyed coca chewing every bit as much as the higher classes, and a certain amount of it

Inca coca pickers
*Coca (*Erythroxylon coca*) was used by the Incas for barter and by the Spaniards to encourage their slaves to mine for gold*

was overlooked as it sustained a very energetic output of manual labour. The Spaniards soon cottoned on to this effect and used coca leaves themselves as encouragement to the reluctant Inca gold miners whom they had enslaved. The alkaloid cocaine was isolated from these leaves in 1860 by Neimann, and its white crystals later glittered in tiny heaps on silver and ivory spatulas at high-society parties in the 1920s, its habit continuing to play a part in the pastimes of the idle rich rather than the out-of-work poor.

While the Portuguese and Spanish were busy on the high seas and the European Renaissance stylishly celebrated their rewards, over English soil the medieval mists took longer to disperse and the Renaissance fire only flickered gradually into life. Having won the Wars of the Roses, Henry VII was busy consolidating the power of the house of Tudor, symbolised by a red and white rose. In 1477, eight years before Henry had come to the throne, Caxton had set up the first printing press in Westminster and between then and 1526 at least sixteen herbals were printed, including Latin versions of works of Dioscorides and Theophrastus. Here was one flicker of the European revival of the Greeks. Another flicker of light was Thomas Linacre, a medical graduate of Padua and Oxford. After his studies in Italy, he returned to Oxford, where he made improved translations of Galen's work. Subsequently he became physician at the royal court, and during the reign of Henry VIII, with the backing of Cardinal Wolsey, he obtained the approval of the king to found the Royal College of Physicians in 1518, becoming its first president.

Provence Rose
Rosa gallica

Dog Rose
Rosa canina

Damask Rose
Rosa centifolia

On the Continent, a physician of a very different calibre was bombastically proclaiming his superiority over all others in the profession. Philippus Aureolus Theophrastus Bombast von Hohenheim – Paracelsus for short – a name he affected to imply that he was at least the equal of Celsus, whose works had been republished fifteen years before Paracelsus' birth in 1493. He was the son of a German doctor who, after becoming a widower, took himself and his only child to a school in southern Austria where he had been appointed to teach chemistry. Paracelsus left this school at the age of fourteen and became one of the wandering students of Europe, drifting in and out of universities, on the lookout for new and progressively-thinking teachers. He always claimed that he completed his education by obtaining a doctoral degree at the University of Ferrara in 1516, and at about this time he set off on a ten-year adventure that took him across Europe and to Russia, England and North Africa. He befriended anyone who seemed 'interesting', preferably magicians, alchemists and necromancers, and returned at the age of thirty-three to his father's home in Villach. He obtained an appointment as lecturer at the University of Basle, embarking on a career of rabble rousing and attention seeking. He pinned on the university noticeboard a proclamation giving the dates of his forthcoming lectures and invited anyone – student or not – to attend. This did not please the authorities who, remembering Luther's similar gesture ten years earlier, began drawing comparisons. Three weeks after this he burned the works of Galen and Avicenna in front of the university. The students loved him for it. The authorities remembered Luther's public burning of the Papal Bull. From our historic viewpoint, he seems reminiscent of the more recent Aleister Crowley, the major difference between them being that Paracelsus was not as good as he thought, and Aleister Crowley was not quite as bad as he hoped people believed. Otherwise they were both very full of themselves and both believed in magic. Paracelsus boastfully claimed that his beard had more experience than the other professors, and that the down on his neck was more learned than his auditors. The magic he believed in was the healing force of nature. He accepted the Hippocratic opinion that a body, given the right conditions, would heal without a lot of complicated remedies, but he believed that the process was magical. He scorned Galen's multi-ingredient medicines, as well as the belief that the various parts of the body and the diseases to which they succumbed were controlled by the stars and planets. This, he claimed, was superstition. This was true, but so was his revival of the old Doctrine of Signatures, which held that diseases should be treated by those plants whose form or habitat most resembled the affected part of the body or the disease itself; *similia similibus curantur* – like cures like. Thus walnuts – brain shaped – were natural remedies for headaches. Hound's-tongue leaves were applied to dog bites. Henbane, with a tooth-shaped seed pod, was given for toothache; cyclamen, with ear-shaped leaves, for earache; saxifrage, which roots itself into rock crevices (seeming to be the cause of the fracture), was believed similarly to break up internal stones. Paracelsus believed too that plants grew where they were needed most – trees to allay fevers by swamps, dockleaves by nettles, and so on. Despite such unsubstantiated notions, he is acknowledged for uniting science with medicine.

Probably due to his father's early influence, he loved experimenting with chemicals, particularly metals, prescribing mineral baths, iron, arsenic, lead and mercury (with which he successfully treated cases of syphilis). He dabbled in tinctures and extracts and prepared opium in the form of a pill or tincture which he called laudanum – a favourite means by which the later Victorians suppressed themselves. He held the principle that

Paracelsus
Philippus Aureolus Theophrastus Bombast von Hohenheim –
Paracelsus for short

83

'what makes a man ill, also cures him', anticipating that of homeopathy. For these things he is remembered as a pioneer of medical chemistry. He died in Salzburg before reaching fifty, still believing in magic.

Ambroise Paré was a far more consistent upholder of Hippocrates. He knew no Latin or Greek, and graduated after four years' practical hospital work in Paris as a barber–surgeon, but he became one of the most outstanding physicians of his day and surgeon to four monarchs. He learned his profession at first hand on the battlefields, travelling with the French armies, and he did *not* believe in magic. Unlike Paracelsus, he would have had no time for the supposed powers of wound ointment, which was a popularly applied form of Sympathetic Magic. This ointment was usually made up of highly imaginative ingredients, including human blood, eunuch's fat (when it could be had) and 'usnea', which was included in pharmacopoeias until the nineteenth century and was the moss scraped from the skulls of hanged men. Sympathetic magic, it may be remembered, does not work directly. Wound ointment, therefore, was not applied to the wound itself but to the weapon that had inflicted it, or its symbol. It often worked, coincidentally, for the simple reason that a wound once cleaned and left alone had more chance of healing than one that had been smeared with a concoction of herbs mixed with lard. Paré ignored such nonsense. He was concerned instead with the serious matter of relieving the suffering of soldiers who, over and above the agonies of amputations, often died from inflammation of these after they had been cauterised with boiling oil. During the capture of Turin, supplies of oil ran dry and Paré experimented instead with poultices made from egg yolk, oil of roses and turpentine. According to his own account, he spent a restless night following these first trials but was delighted when, at daybreak, he visited his patients to find them in little pain and showing no sign of inflammation or swelling. He vowed that he '. . . nor any other should ever cauterise any wounded with gun shot . . .'

Paré's practical mind had no time for another common cure-all – powdered mummy. He knew for one thing that this so-called exotic Egyptian ingredient was often the product of his native France, the remains of bodies from gallows. He said that both forms were equally beneficial, because 'they are none of them any value'. The Paris Faculty of Medicine was outraged on hearing of his views on this highly esteemed dusty resinous matter. Undaunted, Paré said that neither did he believe in Bezoar stone, and made his opinions known to the current monarch, Charles IX. Bezoar stones were, in fact, the intestinal stones of slaughtered animals, usually goats, and, like unicorn horn, were considered to be a powerful antidote to poisoning. Everyone in those days was very concerned with poisoning – especially monarchs. It so happened that Charles IX had a Bezoar stone of which he was very proud and, when Paré told him he was wasting his time with it, the king sent for a condemned prisoner – a cook who was to face death for stealing a few pieces of silver – and suggested to him that he might save his life by co-operating in an experiment of a medical nature. The imprudent cook agreed. He was dosed with a lethal amount of bichloride of mercury and immediately some of the Bezoar stone. The events that followed were horrible, during which the cook loudly regretted his co-operation. Paré witnessed the last hours of the seven that it took the poor cook to die, no doubt regretting also having discounted the monarch's useless antidote. Nevertheless he had been proved right.

Very gradually, the sort of poly-pharmacy that Galen had advocated was being replaced by more rational medicines. But it was so gradual that even a hundred years later a king would die with more than a little assistance from a gang of physicians who genuinely believed that they were dosing him with the best available – and would get away with murder.

Until the middle of the reign of Elizabeth I, England did not own a single useful acre outside the British seas. The Portuguese and Spaniards, with the blessing of the Pope, had the trading rights to the Eastern and Western world respectively and England was obliged to acquire her drugs and knowledge of them from Europe. Charles Cluisius, professor of botany and director of the Imperial Gardens in Vienna, visited England during Elizabeth's reign and probably introduced his Latin translation of a work by the Portuguese physician García d'Orta stationed in Goa, which described many of the Eastern drugs, including china root, bael fruit, black catechu and the age-old hemp and opium. We know that vanilla had already been introduced from Spanish sources – Hugh Morgan, the queen's apothecary, gave Cluisius a gift of some. Other New World drugs were also becoming familiar and the Englishman John Frampton translated a work written on these by the Spaniard Nicholas Monardes, entitling it *Joyful Newes out of the Newe Founded Worlde*. Elizabeth decided that it was high time that England herself took to the waves. Drake was sent off round the world to wrest away some of Spain's trade monopoly and Raleigh to investigate this 'newe founded worlde'.

Drake returned with gold and glory. Raleigh returned from his new English colony in Virginia, with Virginian tobacco and potatoes. In fact, Sir John Hawkins, notorious for his slave-trading activities and leanings towards piracy and acclaimed for his part in the defeat of the Spanish Armada, had introduced these two plants into Europe ten years before. Raleigh brought them back at the end of the 1580s and was responsible for cultivating them; the potato on his Irish estates, the tobacco by the habit of the pipe which he affected.

The potato needs no description, but of course when it was first introduced it was a novelty sold for a high price, and was naturally considered a medicine. The berries of the potato plant, which, like many other fruits in its family (*Solanaceae*), are poisonous, were used in aphrodisiacs and as a cure for impotence. Raleigh's burnt offerings came to make more fortunes than all the gold and stones of the Spanish-held mines. Tobacco had first been noted at the time of Columbus's second voyage, when his physician Chanca observed both tobacco and capsicums in the West Indies. Monardes had recorded it. Aztecs smoked it mixed with American storax and charcoal through reeds or decorated cylinders which they flourished between meal courses as a mark

Tobacco
Nicotiana tabacum
Smoked by the Aztecs in 'tobacos' – pipes

of dignity and wealth. When the Spaniards asked what it was they were smoking, they reasonably enough replied '*tobacos*' – pipes. Jean Nicot, whose name was given to the plant genus (*Nicotiana*), was the French consul in Lisbon and saw it being cultivated in Portugal as early as 1560.

Sir Walter Raleigh does seem, however, to have been among the first Englishmen to encounter curare. On his last voyage, after Elizabeth's death, he was shown a mixture described by the South American Indians as '*urari*' (He to whom it comes, falls) and, rubbing it between his fingers, one of which had a slight cut, he fell down in a giddy faint. Had the dose been stronger, he may never have had to meet his fate at the Tower.

During Elizabeth's reign, a great deal of bickering went on between the physicians and the apothecaries. In an Act of 1555, Queen Mary had given the physicians the right to take legal action against any apothecary who sold faulty or 'evil' drugs, inspect their premises and destroy anything that was not to their prescription. The physicians took advantage of this power over the apothecaries, and began to rely on them more and more to do their work. They used the apothecary shops as consulting rooms and, when called away on home visits, often as far as twenty or thirty miles, they left 'bills' of items for the apothecaries to mix. The apothecaries toed the line – but not uncomplainingly. They themselves were becoming increasingly interested in medical matters, and adept at them. During the physicians' absences they often prescribed and mixed medicines to their own formulae, a practice which was popular with the poorer people who could not afford the high fees of the 'middle man'.

The physicians felt that the apothecaries were dangerously close to over-reaching themselves. *The Urinal of Physick*, published in 1548, included a section criticising the practices of the 'ignorant' apothecaries who 'by their greed and covertness' economised on their mixtures, which '. . . made many times of naughty stuff, or not well prepared, shall not only do little or no good at all, but shall also put the sick Body in hazard of his life . . .'

Also typical of physicians' attitudes towards the apothecaries were those of William Bullein – a relative of Elizabeth – who in his book *Bullein's Bulwarke of Defense Against all Sickness and Diseases* dictated a few pages of guidance to them. Bullein believed that the apothecaries' was an inferior profession, and that they were unsuitable to practise medicine. But he encouraged them to educate themselves in the use of the tools of their trade and to cultivate herb gardens.

William Turner did not need Bullein's patronising encouragements as he had planted a thriving private botanical garden at Kew fifteen years before Bullein's book was published. Although this had no direct connections with the Royal Gardens for which Kew is world famous, the coincidence is striking. Turner was a botanist and physician who as a staunch Reformist had fled England during the reign of Mary, who was doing her best to rid England of the influence of her father, Henry VIII. With the accession of Edward VI, Turner returned to England and was appointed physician to the Duke of Somerset, Lord Protector of the boy king. Somerset ensconced himself in Sion Abbey and established Turner in a house across the river at Kew. Turner was not happy with this situation. He complained that, out of three years of to-ing and fro-ing across the river to attend Somerset, scarcely three weeks had been spent tending his beloved herbs. This did not, however, prevent him publishing a book on herb nomenclature giving their names in Greek, Latin, Dutch and French, with apothecaries' synonyms. His major work was *A New Herball*, published in three parts, which he dedicated to Queen Elizabeth. This included the careful recording of at least 230 English plants and is considered to be the starting point of systematic botany in this country, and Turner its father. Although dubbed scientist, he was not without his superstitions and believed, as Paracelsus had, in the Doctrine of Signatures. He wrote: 'God hath imprinted upon the Plants, Herbs and Flowers, as it were in Hieroglyphics, the very signatures of their vertues . . .'

Later in Elizabeth's reign came John Gerard. He was a friend of Elizabeth's apothecary Hugh Morgan, and had himself cultivated what he called 'a physic garden' off Chancery Lane. The famous *Gerard's Herbal*, published in 1597, was based on a translation already begun of an earlier work by the Belgian Rembert Dodoens, published fifteen years before. To enliven it, Gerard included over 1,500 woodcuts which were in turn copied from German illustrations. Pirated or not, it became a bestseller and must be one of the most often quoted herbals of its day.

With Elizabeth's death in 1603, the Tudor line ended. James of Scotland became King of England, his life apparently one long disease. A sickly childhood was followed by a life martyred to catarrh, indigestion, diarrhoea, piles, rheumatism, gout and a

John Gerard
His has remained one of the best-known herbals but it was based on a translation of a Belgian work

dose of malaria, throughout which he only once resorted to medicine, and died bravely resisting treatment.

It was during James's reign that in 1617 the apothecaries were given their independence from the Grocers' Company by Royal Charter. An apothecary was to serve seven years' apprenticeship, after which the successful passing of an oral examination conducted by a representative of the College of Physicians entitled the candidate to exclusive rights to set up shop as a fully-fledged apothecary. A year after the Society of Apothecaries was formed, the *First London Pharmacopoeia* appeared. It had been planned by the College of Physicians nearly thirty years before, but it was indicative of the rivalry between the two professions that it should be eventually published so soon on the heels of the apothecaries' new independence. The intention was that they should adhere to the established physicians' prescriptions laid down in it, and treat it 'as if it were a sacred religious canon'. The king proclaimed on behalf of the physicians and their pharmacopoeia that '. . . the manner and form prescribed by the said book should be generally and solely practiced by apothecaries and that they should not . . . compound or make any medicines by any other books or dispensatories whatsoever . . .'

This was not the first city pharmacopoeia, and was compiled with reference to others which had already been published in

Europe. Notable among these was the Nuremberg Pharmacopoeia, which later became the official pharmacopoeia of Germany and the Low Countries, and was comparable in importance to the original *Ricettario Fiorentino* (the first official pharmacopoeia of Florence). This was based on the work of Valerius Cordus, the son of a physician–botanist, and who, as a naturalist, demonstrated exceptional knowledge in this field.

The English physicians, having deliberated so long over their publication, seemed to have finalised it in a flurry of haste and with less care than they might otherwise have done. The as-hastily revised edition, which followed seven months later, apologised for the fact that the president of the College of Physicians had not been consulted over the completed first edition, and admitted that this should never have seen the light of day. The physicians graciously accepted that the blame had been the printer's and not theirs. Even so, this in turn was less than perfect, and eight years later a third edition was printed. This, according to the printer's note, was now 'freed from all errors formerly committed by the transcriber and printer'. The title-page stated that the printing was 1627 – it had in fact been printed in 1626. Although the *First London Pharmacopoeia* obviously had its teething troubles, it was the first, despite its specific title, actually to be intended as a national pharmacopoeia. In the year of its first publication, a new and adventurous profession was established.

John Tradescant set sail on 3 June 1618 for the Arctic Circle. He explored the northern coast of Russia, collected and recorded the plants he found, and returned to England three months later. After three years he sailed again, this time to the Mediterranean, bringing back with him many plants which were new to England. He established a garden in south Lambeth, which he filled with botanic curiosities, and was appointed keeper of the garden of Charles I. John Tradescant Jnr, following in his father's footsteps, set sail in 1637 to Raleigh's Virginia and made subsequent voyages in 1642 and 1654, incorporating botanic expeditions to the West Indies. Most familiar of the plants that father and son brought back between them were the cherry laurel, the bilberry, the lilac, the red maple, the tulip tree and probably Virginia creeper and the Michaelmas daisy.

Charles I's botanist–apothecary, John Parkinson, had also held this office at James's court. He owned a shop and garden in Long

John Parkinson
Botanist-apothecary to Charles I

Acre and had succeeded the equally eminent Mathias de l'Obel, whose own herbal had been another major reference of Gerard's and who had personally been consulted to eliminate many of its first errors. In 1629 Parkinson published his *Paradisus Terrestris*, which described '. . . all sorts of pleasant flowers which our English air will permit to be nursed up . . .' and dedicated it to Queen Henrietta Maria. From a pharmaceutical point of view, his major work was the *Theatre of Plants or A Universal and Complete Herbal*, an impressively comprehensive work on the current drugs, published towards the end of his life in 1640.

Not half so scholarly, but by far the most popularly known, is *Culpeper's Herbal*, first published in 1653 and entitled *The English Physician*. Culpeper served only four years of his apothecary's apprenticeship, but claimed the title 'physician' and opened up a practice in 1640 in Red Lion Street, Spitalfields. Culpeper was a man of the people, against the Royalists and therefore without royal patronage. He discredited himself with the College of Physicians by having the audacity to produce his own English translation of their precious *First London Pharmacopoeia*, and four years later his own herbal came out, incorporating 369 medicinal plants which could be grown in England – they being considered by him 'most fit for English bodies'. As a keen astrologer, he

91

designated each plant to a particular influence – for which he was also criticised – describing this as the plant's 'government and virtue':

> Venus lays claim to this herb as her own, and it is under the sign of Aries (cowslip); it is under the dominion of Jupiter (dandelion); it is under the influence of Mercury, hot in the second degree and dry in the first (fenugreek); flags are under lunar dominion (iris).

Despite Culpeper's disfavour with the authorities, his works were written in the interest of the common folk for whom he always spared the time to give assistance and advice, thereby establishing his popularity among them.

More pertinent to the developing science of pharmacy was a translation made in 1657 by Richard Tomlinson of a textbook of pharmacy written by the French court physician Jean de Renou. It defined the new term 'pharmacy', described the apothecary's duties and gave methods of choosing and preparing *materia medica* (pharmaceuticals) which were classified into vegetable, animal

Nicholas Culpeper
Appreciation for Culpeper's writing, and for his work in the interest of all, was demonstrated by his popularity

Drugs being prepared by an apothecary and his apprentice

and mineral. It also gave guidelines for the situation of the apothecary's shop, which should be built 'in a clean, light part of town', and how items should be displayed and stored. It also advised that there should be a window between the back room and the main part of the shop so that the master could observe his apprentices.

After ten years of Cromwell's military dictatorship, Charles I's son was recalled from French exile and merrily restored a monarchy to England. He revived dormant scientific studies by giving a Royal Charter in 1662 to a society for the promotion of 'Physico-Mathematical Experimental Learning'. Among the first members of this Royal Society were Robert Boyle, the Irish scientist whose law established the relationship between volume and pressure of gasses; Christopher Wren, architect; Sir Isaac Newton, mathematician and ponderer on gravity; and Nicasius Le Febvre, who came over to England with Charles II and was appointed Royal Professor of Chemistry.

Meanwhile, something rotten was festering in Denmark, later Sweden, then Holland, and in July 1665, five years into Charles II's reign, the Great Plague broke out in the slums of St Giles's.

Samuel Pepys – another member of the Royal Society – recorded its beginnings on 7 June 1665: 'I did in Drury Lane see two or three houses marked with a red cross upon the doors and "Lord have mercy upon us".' By the end of July the death toll was 2,000 a week, by August 6,000 and by September 7,000. Rats, or rather their fleas, the true culprits, were not suspected. Instead, 400 dogs were slaughtered. Methods for dealing with the plague were little better than those used 300 years before. The physicians either donned similar protective headgear or, more sensibly and generally, fled the city – in rather larger numbers than the apothecaries, which the latter always felt was to their own credit. It was, but also sadly to their detriment, as half the apothecaries of London died too. Bonfires of tobacco were publicly lit in the belief that it would disinfect the air, which of course it did not.

One stalwart who survived, Dr Nathaniel Hodges, is reported to have continued about his daytime business sucking quantities of lozenges made from myrrh, cinnamon and angelica root, secluding himself at night with intemperate amounts of dry white wine. His deliverance was more likely to have been due to good luck rather than good medicine. By the time the plague petered out in the winter months, at least a fifth of the population was dead. The Great Fire the following year is usually described in history books as the great general environmental antiseptic. More relevant to the plague's non-reappearance were the brown rats, foreign invaders who destroyed the native species and apparently did not share their fleas with their black English cousins.

The seventeenth century was a time of great invention in the field of general medicine. While Charles II was still a boy, Sir William Harvey had shown how circulation was controlled by the heart's action. Later, in 1661, Marcello Malpighi furnished the details by seeing with a microscope how blood was passed from arteries to veins by capillaries. Also with a microscope, the Dutchman Anton van Leeuwenhoek was fascinated to notice, fourteen years later, that from the scrapings of his teeth, magnified over 250 times, could be seen '. . . little animals . . . moving about in a most delightful manner . . .' Without knowing it, he was revealing for the first time the hidden enemy, bacteria. Thomas Sydenham, exponent of Hippocrates and sceptical of the College of Physicians' real understanding of medicine, said that the only place to study medicine was at the bedside, and advanced the important point that disease should be distinguished from symptom, and that therefore causes should be determined before treating symptoms. In the same century a dog was kept alive by having air pumped into its lungs after they had been immobilised – artificial respiration. Dogs were also used (guinea pigs had not yet been introduced from South America) in a crude blood transfusion which was relatively successful, and rather more so than one later performed with sheep's blood on a volunteer clergyman.

To return to pharmacy, in 1669 the court physician, Robert Morison, was appointed the first professor of botany at Oxford, having previously been the king's 'botanic professor', and in 1683 the Italian, John Vigani, began teaching the combined subjects of medical botany and pharmaceutical chemistry at Cambridge, later becoming the university's first professor of chemistry. In spite of these individual steps forward, however, practical application of medicines was still frighteningly primitive. In 1685, Charles II died, and with the full co-operation of his physicians, who swore that they would leave no stone unturned in his treatment.

On 2 February, while being shaved, the king was seized with a convulsion and collapsed, probably as a result of a blood clot. First he was bled. An emetic and two purgatives were administered, followed by an enema, containing mallow leaves, violets, beetroot, camomile, fennel, linseed, cinnamon, cardamom, saffron and aloes – among other things. He was given a snuff of powdered hellebore and another of cowslips. He was given, to drink, a mixture of barley water, liquorice and sweet almond, draughts of white wine, a cocktail of absinthe and anise and extracts of thistle leaves, mint, rue and angelica. Internal treatment continued with slippery elm, peony, lavender, lime flowers, lily of the valley, melon seeds and dissolved pearls. The physicians carried on their unholy assault with gentian root, nutmeg, quinine and cloves. They shaved the king's head and rubbed in powdered blistering beetles, meanwhile applying a drawing plaster of Burgundy pitch and pigeon droppings to his feet. They brought in the Bezoar stones – perhaps thinking that he had been poisoned. None of this improved the king's condition even though a special dose of Raleigh's Antidote was forced down his throat and, after four days, during which he apologised for taking such 'an unconscionable time a-dying', the king died, surely with a sigh of relief.

At the beginning of the eighteenth century, the age-old dispute

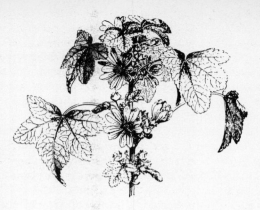

Mallow
Malva sylvestris
Used internally and externally to soothe inflammation

between the physicians and the apothecaries came to a head. In 1703 the Royal College of Physicians took legal action against a member of the Society of Apothecaries, William Rose, whom they accused of prescribing and preparing medicines on his own account, and without reference to one of the 'bills' or prescriptions. They lost their case. The court recognised that it was in the public's interest for apothecaries to prescribe and prepare medicines, effectively giving the individual apothecary the right to choose the emphasis of his particular practice. Some chose to develop their interests by becoming medical practitioners, forerunners of today's GPs, but rather fewer remained as retailers and medicine manufacturers, in company with the comparatively newly-emerged General Association of Chemists and Druggists. One such apothecary was Silvanus Bevan, who opened an establishment at 2 Plough Court, Lombard Street, which had been the birthplace of Alexander Pope. Here he developed a laboratory and founded a flourishing business, which was joined at the end of the century by the young William Allen, whose role in the formation of the present Pharmaceutical Society will later be discussed.

While members of the Society of Apothecaries were going their separate ways, weeds were beginning to overrun their Physic Garden in Chelsea. It had first been planted in 1683 in the tradition of the University Gardens of Bologna, Leiden and Montpellier, but by the end of the century was disorganised and floundering financially. In 1712, the wealthy Dr Hans Sloane, royal physician and member of the Royal Society, became freeholder of the garden's land and ten years later, at the modest lease of £5 a year, guaranteed legally and with the promise of

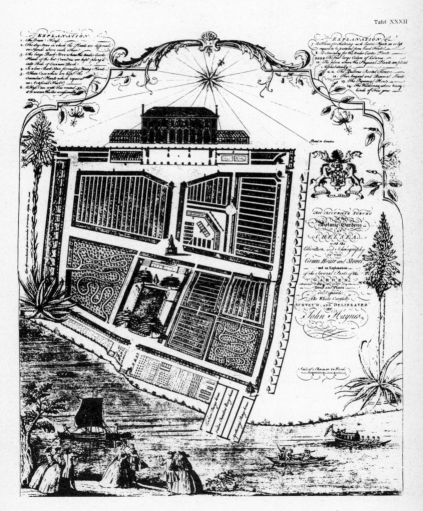

Mid-eighteenth-century plan of the Chelsea Physic Garden

financial assistance that their garden would be allowed to continue and flourish '. . . on the condition that it be forever kept up and maintained by the Company as a Physick garden'.

It was a charming and generous gesture that symbolised the burying of a well-worn hatchet in the gift of a garden. In return, he asked for fifty specimens a year to be delivered to the Royal Society for scientific study. A Swedish botanist came to visit this garden in 1733 and was, by his own account, permitted to collect many plants there. This was Carl von Linné, Linnaeus, founder of modern botanic classification, whose first sight of the gorse on nearby Putney Heath had moved him to kiss the ground at the joy of it. Some unimaginative souls have attempted to suggest that Linnaeus came here in the summer and that, as gorse mainly flowers in the spring, the tale is fanciful. But they obviously did not know that yellow flowers speckle even the thickest blankets of snow on the coldest winter days on Putney Heath, and that gorse is only 'out of bloom when kissing is out of favour'. In any case, it is delightful to think that dear old Putney was able to offer so appropriate a token to so notable a botanic father.

There was another garden. It belonged to the royal country palace at Kew, and it was here that William Pitt came to tell Prince George that his father had died, and that he would be the new king – George III. The Royal Garden, which had largely been developed by the king's mother, Princess Augusta, was designed partly for pleasure and follies, partly for botanic study. William Chambers had been his mother's architectural adviser, and George continued this patronage; as his garden's superintendent he chose the eminent botanist Sir Joseph Banks.

Banks had sailed with Captain Cook on the *Endeavour* in the spring of 1770, and planted the Union Jack at Botany Bay on the newly discovered east coast of Australia. The next summer he returned to England, and the following spring became the unofficial director of the Royal Botanic Gardens at Kew. Once seated in this botanic haven, he was able to enjoy the comforts of armchair botanising, and persuaded the king that rich floral discoveries were to be made in the South African Cape, where he had seen such exotic variations on his voyage with Cook.

He sent a young Kew gardener, Francis Masson, to accompany Cook on his second world voyage as far as Cape Town. Here he was to disembark and explore and botanise for England's posterity. Such expeditions were not without their incident in the early days. Quietly botanising on Table Mountain, Masson was

Joseph Banks
He sailed with Captain Cook and later became unofficial director of the Royal Botanic Gardens at Kew

chased by a gang of escaped convicts. He watched while his companion, Carl Thunberg, plunged with his horse into a hippopotamus pit while attempting to ford a dangerously flooded river. He made a two-and-a-half hour perilous descent down a mountainside, hanging on for all he was worth to the ropes of his wagon to stop it running out of control and tipping out his precious collections. He met the native Bushmen and saw how they made their arrow poison with snake venom and the sap of a species of euphorbia. Three years later, in 1775, he returned to Kew with a splendid collection of plants. This was by no means his last expedition and he sailed again to the Cape, once to the West Indies, and finally to North America, where he died in Montreal two days before Christmas 1805. For all the exotic flora he is accredited with first setting in their glass-house frames, the jolly red geranium is the most familiar cultivated version of the plants brought home by Britain's first officially appointed plant collector.

Sir Joseph Banks not only managed to persuade Masson and

other adventurous souls to risk their safety in the perils of plant collecting, but he also persuaded his protégé, the wealthy young botanist James Edward Smith, to buy the collections and books of Linnaeus after his death in 1778. He himself had been invited to buy these by Linnaeus's widow and, feeling that his personal collections were already close to overflowing, he was quick to convince Smith that such a precious offer was well worth making part of England's heritage. So, for 1,000 guineas, Linnaeus's life's work was bought, and among the valuable cargo that arrived in England from Sweden in 1784 were over 2,500 of his books, huge collections of insects, shells and minerals, as many as 3,000 manuscripts and letters, and approximately 19,000 sheets of pressed plants. Four years after receiving these, Smith founded the Linnaean Society, whose aims were to be 'the cultivation of the Science of Natural History . . . [particularly] of Great Britain and Ireland'.

Where once, before the Renaissance, England had lain on the sheltered edge of a busy world, she was now a well-positioned promontory, eager to take her share of the wealth that the newly expanded globe offered, offering in return such wealth as was being accumulated in her own scientific field. To medicine, the Englishman William Withering gave his *An Account of the Fox-glove*, published in 1785. Ten years prior to this, he had ascer-

Foxglove
Digitalis purpurea
Its action on the heart was first noted by William Withering

tained that the foxglove was the active herb in a country recipe for dropsy, which is the accumulation of fluid beneath the skin and often a symptom of heart disease. He also noted that a brew of foxglove leaves quickened the pulse, and he spent the next few years attempting by innumerable trials to gauge the best form and dosage of this plant to prescribe. He discovered that the active principle was concentrated in the blade of the leaves and that, by slowly drying them in a pan over the coals of the fire in his study, he could produce a powder which he prescribed at approximately four grains a day – a concentration of the drug that is similar to the dosage that would be given today in the same cases.

Withering, with other physicians of his day, considered dropsy to be a disease. It is in fact a symptom of various diseases, heart failure being one of them. It was after Withering's death that it was realised that digitalis was useful only to those suffering from dropsy as a result of heart disease. However, its primary action on the heart was noted, if not fully understood, by Withering, who wrote that digitalis '. . . has a power over the motion of the heart to a degree yet unobserved in any other medicine . . .' It was not until 1869, and in France, that digitoxin was isolated from the crude drug, but the credit for drawing attention to this out-standingly beneficial plant must go to Withering, and to him also the gratitude of all the millions of those whose lives it subsequently prolonged.

William Withering
His An Account of the Foxglove *anticipated how valuable the plant was to become to medicine*

Also in England at the end of the eighteenth century, the country doctor William Jenner, by adhering to the old principle that like cures like, and by himself attending to country wisdom, this time from a milkmaid, made another major discovery. The milkmaid claimed that she was immune from smallpox, having once caught cowpox. To test the validity of this claim, Jenner somewhat precipitately introduced a small amount of cowpox matter into the arm of an eight-year-old boy, and then two months later the same dose of smallpox. Fortunately for the boy, Jenner and for all of us, the experiment was entirely successful and, although his theory, which he proclaimed in 1798, was at first hotly opposed, within little over a year more than seventy physicians signed an article declaring their faith in it, and England eventually made smallpox vaccination (from *vacca* – cow) compulsory in 1853.

Jenner's 'like cures like' principle, demonstrated successfully in the practice of vaccination, was a reflection of another new theory based on the same traditional view and taken to an extreme. Samuel Hahnemann, a doctor from Saxony, had noted that Peruvian bark – the South American cinchona from which quinine comes – produced the same symptoms of feverishness in a healthy body as those that it cured in victims of malarial fever. He reasoned that what was generally regarded as the particular way a disease attacked the body may instead be the body's resistance to the disease and he then began to relate the effects of certain medicinal plants to the symptoms of diseases that they resembled. While testing the strengths of various dosages, it occurred to Hahnemann that the more the drug was diluted, the more potent its effect seemed to become. This apparent reversal of logic, that a thing diminished into virtual non-existence can be a thing strengthened, was such an intriguing and blatant contradiction that it could not fail to fire the imagination, and his ideas attracted popular support. They were not so popular with the more orthodox members of the medical profession, who regarded the general notion as a plain illogicality and furthermore a fraud. Popular opinion, however, prevailed, and homeopathy, as his invention became known, has been adopted throughout the world. It never did gain the respectable status of becoming an orthodox practice, upon which its success was luckily never dependent. Instead it has become the most respected and probably familiar practice of all alternative medicine and, through its royal patronage, an eminent one.

At the time that Withering published his work on digitalis, making medicine was still a crude affair, even though its history was thousands of years old. In the ordinary apothecary's shop, vegetable or new chemical raw materials were prepared with the uncomplicated mortar and pestle, and dispensed as mixtures, powders or compounds. Pills were handrolled, making dosage difficult to measure. It was still a homely business. But advances in medical chemistry soon accelerated a change in the practice of pharmacy that compounded all factions of knowledge from the medical professions, introducing an industry that laid claims to all realms of medicine and made for itself a pharmaceutical empire.

The French apothecary, Nicolas Lemery, had been the first, at the beginning of the century, to apply extraction processes to crude drugs. His work was developed by the Swedish apothecary, Scheele, who worked with both inorganic and organic materials, and published a great deal of information on acids, sugars and other active parts of them. Scheele also discovered the vital life force that keeps us all going – oxygen. The first alkaloids were discovered at the beginning of the nineteenth century. In 1803 narcotine was obtained from opium by the French pharmacist, Derosne, and in 1816 the German, Friedrich Serturner, isolated morphine from the same source, having first recognised it more than ten years before. Within the next three years, strychnine and brucine were isolated from nux-vomica seeds and quinine was obtained from cinchona bark by the Frenchmen Pelletier and Caventou, who in 1820 derived colchicine from the autumn crocus. In 1819, Rudolph Brandes took atropine from belladonna. The homely business would never be the same again, and it is appropriate to take a final glance at the old-style apothecary's shop before progress closed its dusty shutters.

Weighing scales, a counter, bottles, jars and a pungent smell were the dominant features. Aromas of lavender and storax mingled with eau-de-Cologne made from essences of neroli, lemon, rosemary and the citric bergamot. The commonest medicines were mixtures, which accounted for about 40 per cent of medicaments. Pills were next in popularity, and were pasted with resins and oils. Favourites were those containing opium or ginger and it was common for them to be rolled in liquorice powder as a coating. Powders were prescribed to be taken with rose-leaf tea, lemon or barley water, or with a spoonful of honey or marmalade. Ointments, which were still by far the smallest stock, were based on oils and waxes and included white lead and camphor and sometimes opium. A special Black Drop was on sale, having three times the strength of laudanum, and a Black Mixture, also known as Black Draught and Black Dose. But there was scarcely any sense in concealing the ingredient. Opium was, in any case, freely prescribed and jars of poppy heads were there to be made into teas for headaches. Pills cost about a penny or less each. Powders were about twopence and ointments half a shilling an ounce. Toothpaste bordered on the cosmetic rates at two shillings for four ounces. Perfumed waters became more expensive when they included musk and ambergris (from the deer and the whale) and sold for over five shillings, sometimes even ten. Leeches went for sixpence each and blood letting as a service was practised. Some proprietary brands of salts and cough medicines were sold, and a few condiment delicacies such as anchovy sauce and curry powder. Household cleaners, poisons for pests and powders for pets all changed hands over the polished wood counter and marble slab. The little high-street apothecary's shop is now no more than a novelty museum exhibit. It is a pity, for there is scarcely one of us that would not relish an afternoon in such an establishment. Of course, they did not close, but they changed. They became depersonalised, more retail-oriented and more like businesses than practices. It is difficult not to regard these changes with regret, and to feel, sentimentally, that there has been something lost of the homeliness of medicine, especially in the light of the laboratory conditions that we know go with the making of today's drugs. But in the nineteenth century and in the hundred-odd years that have followed, pharmaceutical knowledge has become more complete more quickly than at any other time in history, and any regret that we have for the past must be balanced against the gratitude that each of us owes to modern medicine.

5

Pharmacists and Plant Hunters

When William Withering published his *An Account of the Foxglove* in 1785, he was duly honoured by the medical professions in Britain, France and Germany and subsequently elected a member of the Royal Society and the Linnaean Society. However, one particular doctor was not so pleased by these events. Dr Erasmus Darwin had published a paper on the same subject at the beginning of the year, and was extremely put out at the fact that he was not considered the first to give an account of the plant's properties. Fortunately, everyone in the profession was well aware that Darwin's 'own' paper had been based on previous commentaries by Withering (although Darwin had made no mention of his sources) and he was denounced as a priority stealer. Darwin had to retire disgruntled.

He continued with his book *Zoonomia, or the Laws of Organic Life*, which speculatively proposed that animal life might have originated from the same primitive state and developed as a consequence of environmental changes. History very nearly repeated itself. Erasmus's grandson, Charles Darwin, was considerably panicked on reading in *The Annals and Magazine of Natural History* (1855) that a younger man, the traveller and naturalist Alfred Wallace, was perilously close to coming to the same conclusions that he himself had been working on for twenty years. He wrote to his friend, the geologist Charles Lyell, that he hated the idea of writing for priority, but that '. . . I certainly would be vexed if anyone were to publish my doctrines before me . . .'

Three years later, Wallace, in a letter to Darwin, outlined exactly the same theory of natural selection that Charles had arrived at, asking him to show it to others if he thought it was any good. Charles Darwin was greatly perturbed. He felt that all his originality was in danger of being pre-empted, but he was a gentleman and more ethical than his grandfather. Rather than grabbing the limelight to the detriment of his rival, he declared that he would prefer to burn his entire book than have Wallace or any other think he had behaved in a paltry spirit. Luckily, his friends, Lyell and the son of the director at Kew Gardens, Joseph Hooker, honourably settled the matter for him in July 1858 by publicly presenting both his and Wallace's papers, together with a letter summarising his theory written the year before to the American botanist Asa Gray. The next year, Darwin's *On the Origin of Species* sold out on the first day of publication and the author's success was assured.

On his five-year trip on the *Beagle* at the beginning of the 1830s, during which he first glimpsed the truth of natural selection on the Galapagos Islands, Charles Darwin's status is usually recorded as that of ship's naturalist. This is not entirely true. In the 1760s and 1770s, Captain Cook had eradicated the curse of scurvy (vitamin C deficiency) from long sea voyages by introducing compulsory sauerkraut to the ship's menu and dosing those already suffering with orange and lemon jellies. What Cook had not been able to alter was the dreadful boredom and isolation

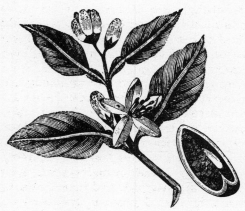

Orange
Citrus sinensis
One of the fruits, rich in vitamin C, used by Captain Cook to prevent scurvy in his crews

106

experienced during such voyages. The object of the voyage of the *Beagle* was to complete the survey of Patagonia and Tierra del Fuego, to survey the shores of Chile, Peru and some Pacific islands, and to carry a chain of chronometrical measurements round the world. The purpose of Darwin's being aboard was to keep Captain Fitzroy company. True, Darwin was engaged as a supernumerary naturalist – there was another already aboard, the surgeon–naturalist McKormick – but Captain Fitzroy was concerned with the psychological trials of being alone in charge of a company of men with whom his rank dictated he could not mix socially.

His fears were not unfounded. The previous captain had shot himself after three years afloat, and Fitzroy's uncle had demonstrated a family instability by cutting his own throat. Fitzroy feared for his own sanity and prior to the trip began to look for a gentleman of similar social standing to share his mealtimes on board. He was introduced to Darwin. This young man soon outstripped the collecting efforts of McKormick, whom he considered 'an ass' (the 'ass' was put ashore at Rio), returning home five years later with a fine natural history collection, an intriguing notion and Captain Fitzroy still intact. When he later learnt of the conclusions that Darwin had reached on board his ship, poor Captain Fitzroy never quite forgave himself for what he believed was his neglect in not diverting his former companion from such blasphemy, and was seen at the presentation of Darwin's and Wallace's theories brandishing the Bible aloft and crying out, 'The book, the book!' From remorse or the instability that he had so feared, probably both, he followed his uncle's lead and five years later cut his throat.

Of course, at the time, the theory of natural selection was not by any means universally accepted. It still is not today. Darwin himself never relinquished his belief in God and Wallace died a staunch spiritualist, but their theory marked an historic stage of scientific innovation that has endured. Superstition endures too, and quackery – but they are no longer controlling elements. Darwin represents a figurehead around which gathered the most notable scientists of his day and, had he and Wallace not been there to proffer what they did, some other would surely have done so instead. As the brilliant medic and educator, Thomas Huxley, commented, 'How extremely stupid not to have thought of that.' Although Darwin had trained in medicine, he was not a doctor as such, yet the influence of his theories was far-reaching in the field both conceptually and practically. He was not a specialist in botany – in fact it was one of his weaker subjects, and one in which he turned to Hooker and Asa Gray for guidance – yet he beautifully demonstrated what Linnaeus had illustrated. He was the sign of the times. This was the eve of the twentieth century, and it dawned gradually but inevitably. In the twenty years that Darwin took carefully to formulate his theories, other events were taking place that contributed to the modern age. Some were to the positive good, some were equally bad, which nevertheless by their character were such glaring mistakes that they became lessons for improvement. Such were the Opium Wars.

The year was 1839. The young Queen Victoria had been on the throne for two years and since the time of Elizabeth Britain had developed an empire that would soon control a quarter of the world, both in acres of dry land and in numbers of population. In the circumstances, it was down to Britain to set some good examples. On the home front, some unpardonable wrongs had been put to rights: Catholics were now allowed to stand for parliament; the 'middle classes' (men only, of course) were given the right to vote; slavery had been abolished; children under the age of nine were no longer allowed to work in factories, and the Poor Law Amendment Act made it the duty of the state to care for the underprivileged (not that the workhouse was an attractive alternative to the worst conditions of manual fieldwork, but it

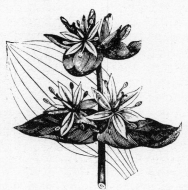

Yellow Gentian
Gentiana lutea
Also known as bitter root, this plant has most commonly been used, since the Middle Ages, as a tonic

was a step in the right direction). The circumstances that precipitated the Opium Wars reflect scandalously against Britain, revealing the shady side of her powerful East India Company and proving it to be as much a company of drug pushers as one of honourable commercial traders.

Although opium had been referred to in ancient China, it never seems to have been a traditional crop. The original poppy (*Papaver setigerum*) was native to the Mediterranean regions, and the cultivated species which we know today as the opium poppy (*Papaver somniferum*) was taken from there to Italy, Egypt and Arabia. Persia had it by the ninth century AD and took it to India. It was first introduced commercially into China by the Arab and Turkish traders in the late seventh century AD. From then until the seventeenth century it remained a medicinal drug to relieve pain and tension. At this stage, tobacco was brought to China from America, the Chinese mixed the two drugs and opium smoking became the rage. As early as 1730, the Chinese emperor, alarmed at the deleterious effects of the habit, banned it. But bad habits once adopted are not so easily quashed, particularly when large profits are to be made from them. The present tobacco trade in Britain is tolerated not so much because we are a democracy or that it is an old tradition, but because it is extremely profitable.

In the 1770s the East India Company, seeing how well the Portuguese were faring by selling Indian opium in China, began to do the same. They established a monopoly of opium growing in Bengal and began to support the Chinese habit themselves. It was easy money. How they justified this can only be wondered at; perhaps they did not bother to. There can be absolutely no question that they somehow believed that to have acted otherwise would have been to deprive China of a useful drug. They knew exactly what they were doing and, worse, were surreptitious about it in not handling the drug themselves. The East India Company invented a neat trading loop whereby private traders, licensed by themselves, took their opium for them from India and passed it on to Chinese smugglers in exchange for gold and silver. This was then handed over to officials of the Company in the southern port of Canton, who in turn made payment by bills of exchange for English currency, using their ill-gotten gold and silver to buy Chinese tea and silk for export to England. As the East India Company's profits flourished, so opium addiction increased. By Victoria's reign, Britain had become inordinately fond of opium herself, and in one way or another was consuming in the region of 60,000 pounds of it yearly. England's apparent unconcern at this alarming trend may perhaps explain in some small degree her lack of conscience over her overseas activities. This is not, however, to excuse them.

There was a world of difference between the comparatively genteel laudanum sippers of England and the hardened opium smokers of China. The botanist and adventurer, Robert Fortune, watched, fascinated, one dawn, an untidy heap of snoozing Chinese who bore no resemblance whatsoever to similarly subdued occupants of Victorian drawing-rooms:

> There was the habitual opium smoker – there was no mistaking him – his looks were pale and haggard, his breathing quick and disturbed, and so thin was he that his cheekbones seemed to be piercing his skin. Some seemed care-worn with business, and others again apparently slept soundly with hearts light and joyous. All had the foreparts of their heads shaved and their tails lay about in wild confusion.

The Chinese government, in an attempt to stop Britain's illegal trading, confiscated all opium found in Canton. A Chinese villager was murdered by some drunken British sailors who were given protection from Chinese justice by the British government. The first opium war broke out. Britain won and an uneasy settlement was agreed, but Britain still did not have the rights to the extent of trade that she wanted. In 1856, war broke out again, this time the French joining forces with the British, and four years later the Chinese were forced to back down. They signed an agreement legalising Britain's import of opium, or rather making official what Britain had in any case been doing for well over fifty years, during which time she had increased the amount of opium she was supplying to China sixty-fold. It was not a noble victory.

Fortunately, not all Britain's drug trading tells such a tale of blatant racketeering and, so long as we do not dwell on some of the grim conditions suffered by those employed for a pittance to harvest the empire's wealth, the tale is a romantic one. Since the Elizabethan era, London had developed a drug market that was rivalled only by that of Amsterdam. Mincing Lane and Mark Lane, which lead down to the Thames from Fenchurch Street, became the busiest commercial area in the city. In the seventeenth century, merchants thronged the coffee houses, arranging transactions with each other. The Jerusalem Coffee House was a

Coffee
Coffea arabica
Coffee houses remained the favourite trading places of the drug merchants

particular haunt of those concerned with Eastern trade, while traders specialising in West Indian merchandise haggled over prices in the Jamaica Coffee House; tea was first taken – and priced – at Garraway's. At the beginning of the eighteenth century, the East India Company instituted its first quarterly drug auctions and a hundred years later the original London Commercial Sale Rooms were founded in Mincing Lane. However, the more formal atmosphere of these premises did not suit the drug merchants, who were used to the cosiness and familiarity of their coffee-table bartering, and they took their business to the more convivial surroundings of the New Corn Exchange Tavern, where trading continued until the Sale Rooms were rebuilt at the end of the century.

In the nineteenth century, the East and West India (up-river) Docks bustled with activity, the smell of the muddy Thames mingling with the mustiness of damp sacking and trodden straw. Socotrine aloes arrived packed in monkey skins; Curaçao aloes in globular gourds. Hessian sacks of senna; bales of cinnamon, raffia-wrapped; South American sarsaparilla in cowhide 'seroons'; cases of cascara – all were garbled, graded and repacked in the warehouses on the docks. Kerosene cans of Peru balsam and drum storax from Turkey were rolled along the quays to points of inspection. Flasks of Bulgarian rose oil were unstoppered and sniffed, blocks of black opium weighed in. All a heady contrast to the English air.

Today the London Docks are dead. What merchandise still comes by ship is unloaded on the down-river docks in uniform containers and lifted by cranes, not human porters. St Katharine's Dock, once a predominant point of drug imports, is now a glittering social playground, flanked by novelty shops, wine bars and restaurants. Local street names still conjure past tradings: Pepper Street, Saffron Hill, Hemp Walk, Rum Close; Clove Street – a little to the north – Cinnamon Street – more easterly. Few pharmacists today will have experienced the wholesale activities of what still comprises a part of their stock-in-trade, but the first students of the school of the Pharmaceutical Society were encouraged to learn for themselves, in the warehouses of the East End, what went into the making of their medicines.

Among others, two particular issues were presented to parliament for consideration in 1841. One, sponsored by the physicians, was concerned with settling current disputes between the affiliated interests of the apothecaries-turned-medical practitioners and the physicians, and those of the newly expanding body of chemists and druggists. The second issue was the future organisation and direction of the Royal Botanic Gardens at Kew.

Since the Rose Case of 1703, which had set a precedent for their

Pepper
Piper nigrum
Pepper Street, near St Katharine's Dock in London, conjures scenes of former local commerce

rights in the practice of general medicine, those apothecaries who chose to take that direction left behind them their former prerogatives over pharmaceutical practices. These were inherited by the chemists and druggists, or the (now minority) group of apothecaries who retained an interest in pharmacy rather than general medicine. The apothecaries' Act of 1815 had favourably clarified the trading rights of chemists and druggists; they were allowed to buy, prepare, dispense and sell drugs or medicines and their compounds in both a retail and wholesale capacity. However, by 1841, although their new interests left less time for pharmaceutical matters, the medical apothecaries were expressing concern over the standard of qualifications held by those to whom these matters had been relinquished. Although the chemists and druggists had formed themselves into an association in 1802 which had been refounded on an enlarged scale in 1829, they could not claim that a formal education had been received, or a full apprenticeship served, by all of their members and thus could not declare themselves an organised pharmaceutical profession. This was an obvious point of attack. Another was the evidence of drug alteration seen in both wholesale and retail trade, perpetrated at source or prior to the drugs being handed over the counter – already an historic part of medical chicanery.

The apothecaries' 1815 Act did not give them supervisory rights over the pharmaceutical practices of the chemists and druggists – now they claimed them. The chemists and druggists naturally wanted to remain free of professional restrictions. The better qualified and already successful of the chemists and druggists were equally concerned at the fact that the pharmaceutical knowledge of some of their colleagues left a lot to be desired, for it reflected, they felt, on themselves, and jeopardised their standing in the eyes of both the public and their medical associates. The time had come for some serious re-organisation to be affected.

Jacob Bell, whose father ran a well-thought-of and well-organised pharmaceutical establishment in Oxford Street, began a series of debates between chemists, druggists and medical men. They were held in the comfort of his Oxford Street home, in a tea party atmosphere. The discussion at the first of these so-called 'pharmaceutical tea parties', held in March 1841, centred on the progress through parliament of the proposed Bill which, had it been passed, would have effectively put the chemists and druggists under the partial control of the medical apothecaries, and limited their professional responsibilities.

The next month, at the Crown and Anchor Tavern in the Strand, a general assembly of chemists and druggists met with their committee who were reporting on events in parliament. It was decided to carry out previous proposals and to form a society, the aims of which were to elevate the association to the standing of a self-governing and educated professional organisation and by its efforts to give pharmacy a firm scientific basis.

The names of those at the historic Crown and Anchor meeting were later to become familiar to subsequent members of the Pharmaceutical Society, the foundation of which can be said to date from this occasion. Of course, Jacob Bell and his father John Bell were present. William Allen was there, now in his seventies, whose scholastic and scientific activities had greatly assisted the old Plough Court pharmacy of Silvanus Bevan into becoming a flourishing business. His nephew and partner in what had now become a family firm, Daniel Bell Hanbury, was with him. He had worked at the Plough Court pharmacy since his apprenticeship at the age of fourteen, had become a partner in 1824 and remained there until his retirement at the age of seventy-four. At the time of the Crown and Anchor meeting, his own son, also Daniel Hanbury, was soon to enter Plough Court as an apprentice, later becoming an active member of, and lecturer at, the Pharmaceutical Society. He was known for his outstanding efforts in the scientific field of medical botany, for which he was awarded the honour of becoming a fellow of the Royal Society.

In December 1841, the new Pharmaceutical Society of Great Britain rented the premises at 17 Bloomsbury Square as their headquarters, and held their first council meeting the following January. One of the first decisions reached by the council, under the presidency of William Allen, was that a school of pharmacy should be established. If they wished their profession to be acknowledged as a leading authority on drugs, they must make certain that all students educated by their Society received the very best instruction in all aspects of pharmacy. It was important that new pharmacists should be knowledgeable about crude drugs, which they dealt with in various forms. It was decided that two of the most important items on the school's curriculum, besides chemistry, should be botany and materia medica. This latter study was concerned with the botanic origins, the history and the character of crude drugs and had been redefined in a small work, *Analecta Pharmacognostica*, by Seydler in 1817. Besides familiarising the pharmacist with the tools of his trade, the purpose of pharmacognosy – from the Greek *pharmakon* (a drug) and *gignosco* (to acquire a knowledge of) – was to enable pharmacists to detect adulterated and sub-standard drugs, and so rid the market of them. In the subject were incorporated all the elements that were to develop into the sciences of botany and plant chemistry. What better allies could the Pharmaceutical Society have had at that time than the botanic scientists of the newly state-controlled gardens at Kew? This was to become a close and enduring association, bonded in co-operation and friendship.

By the time that Victoria came to the throne, royal involvement with the gardens at Kew was less than it had been when Caroline, queen of George II, first lavished such attention and expenditure on the grounds. The days were gone when Princess Augusta had been seen floating in a swan-shaped boat on the lake there at the celebrations of her teenage son's birthday, or when, as the middle-aged monarch George III, he was witnessed stumbling across the gardens after the swiftly fleeing Fanny Burney, an attendant to the queen. Although the Duke of Cumberland, who had been elected to the Hanoverian throne, still retained his house there and the Duke of Cambridge occupied a residence on the south side of Kew's green, the royal presence was no longer as evident as it had been. William Aiton, who superintended the gardens, had not been a favourite of the previous monarch, William IV, and in 1837 his general popularity suffered as criticisms were levelled against the running of the gardens and his management of them. The following year questions were being asked in parliament. Was the best use being made of the Royal Gardens in the way of furthering botanic study? Were the collections already there being maintained and labelled efficiently, and what improvements could be made to them by additions and expansions? Should they be put in the charge of the Horticultural Society, some of whose members, headed by Dr John Lindley, had already conducted an enquiry into the current conditions of all the chief royal gardens, Kew included? Should parliament, as had been suggested, take control of the gardens and develop them into a national institution for research into medical and economic botany? Parts of the gardens were already open to the public, but it was felt that the botanic section could be improved and made much more interesting to the public and students of botany alike, rather than let it remain as a place for chiefly specialist study. Parliament reached a decision on the matter and the Royal

Gardens were handed over to the Commissioners of Woods and Forests in March 1840. Aiton retired that November and the following spring, a year after they had become state property and the sole responsibility of the government, the Royal Botanic Gardens were officially put under the directorship of Sir William Hooker.

The year 1841, when the first official director of Kew was appointed, was, as we have seen, the most active time in the foundation of the Pharmaceutical Society of Great Britain. It also saw Britain at the height of her empire's glory. The Opium Wars were still a current issue, but this crisis had little serious effect on the flourishing sea trade that Britain enjoyed, only serving to hamper some exploratory voyages. Much of the empire's wealth of plant resources was already freely available for examination and study by pharmacists and botanists; more wealth still awaited discovery. It was, in every sense, an age of collection and cultivation – and a time of learning.

From the point of view of materia medica, or pharmacognosy as it became known, the most useful teaching aid that the

William Hooker
The first Director of the Royal Botanic Gardens, Kew

116

Pharmaceutical Society's new school of pharmacy could offer its students was a collection or museum of drugs, which would exhibit preserved specimens of their plant sources in various stages of growth, their crude forms and their different stages of manufacture. The beginning of the Pharmaceutical Society's museum was described in the *Pharmaceutical Journal* of 2 February 1878, which reported proudly on the museum's developments since its anniversary thirty-six years before:

> It was a front room on the ground floor [17 Bloomsbury Square] containing not a vestige of furniture. The bare boards were well scoured, the ceiling and walls were in a perfect state of repair, but there was not in it even a chair or a table. On the floor, in one corner, was a small heap of brown paper parcels, containing a few donations from two or three of its [the Society's] members and on the mantelshelf were about a dozen glasses and bottles in which were sundry crystals, roots and other substances. These formed the nucleus of what is now perhaps the most complete collection of materia medica in the world.

A little over a year after the small row of bottles and the few brown paper parcels had been left in the otherwise empty room, the museum's first curator, Theophilus Redwood, was able to report that it now boasted well over 800 specimens. By the time that the 1878 anniversary tribute was written, the museum had inherited 500 specimens that had formerly been used to illustrate the talks of the late Dr Jonathan Pereira, one of the school's first and most distinguished lecturers. The museum also incorporated an even larger contribution from Pereira's most accomplished student, Daniel Hanbury, who had died in 1875. There was a collection of old English drugs, a Chinese collection, donations of Indian drugs from Professor Dymock, a surgeon–major in the Bombay Army, and others from Australia, the Americas and Africa.

Those first fifty years of the Pharmaceutical Society marked a singular stage in the museum's growth. It was special because of the scholastic attention paid to each new acquisition and the goodwill with which each was sent. This was conveyed in the correspondence and written research accompanying many of them, which also highlighted the mutual interest and willing co-operation between those who gave and those who received specimens. These donors' names (once familiar signatures among the correspondents) are now printed side by side in acknowledgement of their historic importance. But what has been preserved since then is a sense of the fascination with which these gifts were first viewed for their novelty – as these same things are now fascinating for their antiquity.

Among the treasures that came to the museum in its early days were, of course, many from Kew Gardens. More than one hundred assorted extracts, gums, resins, woods and seeds were received, bearing the director's compliments. They included arrowroot starch from St Vincent in the West Indies (1879); a dried cocoa pod (1876); a stem from the 'true myrrh tree of Arabia', collected sixty miles from Aden (1878); the bark of white mulberry, its leaves food for silkworms, bearing the Japanese name *Kawa-no-no-no-kawa*; jackass tree gum gathered in Sierra Leone and cashew tree gum (1883); and sandalwood from the Sandwich Islands.

The name of Kew's director in these cases was Joseph Dalton Hooker, the first director's son, who, as his father had been in 1836, was awarded a knighthood for outstanding achievements in botany. Both were keen collectors, but Joseph became the active partner in this while Sir William established, at home, the gardens as he had envisaged them – a centre for botanic study and the ornamental display of a science. Joseph began his scientific career on a Royal Navy ship, HMS *Erebus*, which cruised the southern ocean. During this and other voyages, he searched for his own 'origins of species', as Charles Darwin, whom he

Round Kaempferia or Zedoary
Kaempferia rotunda
Used in a similar way as ginger for digestive disorders

118

championed, did his, and it was appropriately to him that Charles Darwin first outlined his theory. He embarked on his great Himalayan expedition at the beginning of 1848, starting off

Joseph Hooker
Botanist and plant collector, he inherited his father's position as Director of the Royal Botanic Gardens, Kew

overland from Calcutta in fine style, with an entourage of attendants, a team of elephants and cattle to take his luggage. When he arrived in Sikkim, he was astonished at the magnificence of the rhododendrons, but he met such open hostility there that he was lucky to escape with his life – besides enough seeds to sow great bushy patches of colour in the borders of Britain's stately homes. Five years before he became the second director of the gardens in 1865, he went with his friend, Daniel Hanbury, on another expedition to the Holy Land, from which journey the museum preserved many herbarium sheets. Even at the age of sixty, as an established scientific figure and by then a knight, Sir Joseph did not hesitate to relinquish the comforts of his study to make camp in the great outdoors of the Rockies of Colorado in another great collecting expedition. There is a photograph in the Herbarium Library, Kew, which shows him at La Veta Pass, in a forest clearing where a tall tent stood, supported by a stout stripped sapling against the backdrop of spruce trees. He is seen seated beside his friend, the American botanist Asa Gray, who had, besides pursuing his botanising activities in

Daniel Hanbury
A member of the 'Scientific Committee for the Promotion of Pharmacological Knowledge' and of the Pharmaceutical Society. He published more than fifty papers on the crude drugs commonly used in his day.

common with Hooker's, devoted himself to propagating Darwin's ideas in his country. In the picture, Asa Gray, cross-legged on the grass below Hooker, is holding his plant press while Hooker holds a specimen sprig, and at their feet is a pile of cones and branchlets for inspection. Other members of the party are gathered behind these two figures around a white-clothed table. A servant bringing a water jug and hand towel and a guide in a fringed skin jacket, Davy Crockett-style, are in attendance. The scene epitomises the Victorian Great White Collector.

Daniel Hanbury, although extensively travelled, was not the first-hand collector that Joseph Hooker was. He did not have the other's hardiness or stamina, and instead acquired his collection of drugs from fellow botanists and travellers, or from well-established foreign pharmacies and botanic institutions. Hanbury's main concern was in finding out facts. Once set on an investigative course, he pursued the matter until his journey of discovery was complete. He wrote to the great collector of South American flora, Richard Spruce, with whom he had much correspondence: 'You see I am nearly mad on this subject [the correct location of the source of Peru balsam], but the fact is, I do not soon abandon anything, once taken in hand.' His tenacity was particularly displayed by his energies in clarifying the misconceptions that prevailed on the subject of storax, many samples of which, once belonging to him, subsequently became the property of the museum. By far the best of these was a five-pound block of drum storax, which resembled a solid brown cake of sugar mixed with treacle, and smelled of cinnamon and vanilla (the balsam is rich in cinnamic acid, contains vanillin and in its solid form develops a crystallised texture).

Storax was an old remedy for cases of asthma, bronchitis, catarrh and other pulmonary troubles, taken internally or as an inhalant, and was also used in ointments for skin disorders. Problems of the identification of the source of storax were partly due to the several commercial names used for it, depending on its stage of preparation when presented: Levant storax; liquid storax (Styrax Liquida); prepared storax (Styrax Praeparatus); Styrax Balsam; Styrax Calamita; amygdaloid storax (Styrax Amygdaloides); storax *rouge-brun* or storax *en pain* (*Guibourt*); black storax; and drop or gum storax. This variety of terms, coupled with the fact that another, similar substance – though of different botanical origin, *Styrax officinale L.* – had been collected and used in the same way since ancient times and referred to by the same name, did much to confuse the issue of the botanical origins of the substance.

The earliest allusion to storax occurs in the writings of Aetius and Paulus Aegineta, Greek physicians living in the sixth and seventh centuries AD respectively, and they describe two forms of the substance, namely storax and liquid storax. Until the end of the eighteenth century, solid storax (Storax Solidus) and liquid storax (Styrax Liquida) were names used to differentiate between the balsam of *Styrax officinale* and that of *Liquidambar orientalis* but, as the former became scarcer and finally ceased to be used in commerce, the description solid storax continued to be applied to any solid form of the latter, and so was presumed to come from the same tree. Needless to say, as the botanical name *Styrax officinale* seemed to imply it was the official source of storax, the problem was compounded.

In the US Pharmacopoeia, storax had been erroneously

ascribed to *Styrax officinale* from 1831 to 1863. A Professor Krinos of Athens had published information in a Greek newspaper determining that the storax seen in trade was obtained from *Liquidambar orientalis* and this had been repeated in 1855, but no attention had been paid to this information in western Europe. However, Krinos had also proposed that the modern source had also been used anciently – which was not as Hanbury believed.

This problem too must have driven Hanbury 'nearly mad', but he was determined to settle the matter once and for all, and he did so in 1857 by publishing an article in the *Pharmaceutical Journal* entitled 'On Storax'. It began: 'Having in a former issue brought under review the various opinions current as to the origins of liquid storax and stated the points on which I consider them erroneous, I will now proceed to communicate the information which I have myself received regarding the drug from three valued correspondents in the Levant.' These were Sidney Maltass of Smyrna (Izmir), Lieutenant R. Campbell, Consul on the island

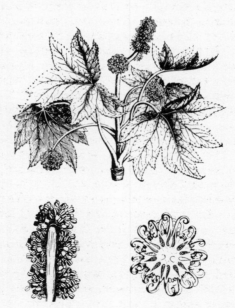

Storax
Liquidambar orientalis
The subject of an article by Daniel Hanbury which distinguished between the ancient and modern sources of this drug

of Rhodes, and Dr James McCraith of Smyrna. They had provided several samples of variations of so-called storax and specimens from the trees from which these resins were obtained. All tests and examinations of these revealed them to be from *Liquidambar orientalis*. Hanbury concluded his article in which he had given a detailed description of the cultivation, collection and commercial preparation of storax with the following statements: 'That the original and classical storax was produced by *Styrax officinale L.* That always scarce and valuable it had in modern times wholly disappeared from commerce. That liquid storax is the produce of *Liquidambar orientalis* and that it is collected in the south-west of Asia Minor.'

Subsequent reports on the collecting of storax have differed in details from Hanbury's, but probably only as a result of its having been observed in different regions or in a more recent time. However, there is agreement on the traditional method; in the early summer the trees were beaten or punctured. As a pathological response, a resin formed in the inner bark or cortex. Later in the year, often in the autumn, the outer bark was removed and the inner bark scraped from the trees and pressed to extract any surplus resin. The pressed bark would then be boiled in sea water and pressed again through horse-hair sacks to separate the resin. The crude balsam thus obtained was a greyish viscid substance, with a pleasant aromatic odour suggestive of cinnamon and almonds, which always contained water and vegetable fibres. This was crude storax, much of which was exported to India (Bombay) and China from Rhodes, where it had been shipped from Izmir. The remaining bark was dried and described as Cortex Thymiamatis or storax bark and used locally or in other parts of south-west Asia as a fumigant. A further product was obtained by mixing the coarsely ground Cortex Thymiamatis in a proportion of 2:3 with crude storax. It was packed in wooden drums or cans and shipped from Izmir to Athens, Venice, Marseilles and, chiefly, Trieste, and was known commercially as Styrax Calamita, drum storax gum, drop storax, or amygdaloid storax. Purified storax, or styrax, was prepared from the crude storax by warming and straining it, or by dissolving it in alcohol and then filtering and evaporating it – the method employed to make Styrax Praeparatus or prepared storax of pharmacy.

American storax, more recent in trade, was collected from *Liquidambar styraciflua L.*, the sweet gum, and cultivated in Central America, chiefly Honduras, and to a lesser extent Guatemala. It was a product similar to Asian storax but in its case the balsam exuded into natural pockets between the bark and the wood in older trees and thus beating or puncturing them to precipitate a flow was not necessary. The natural pockets, which could contain up to eight pounds of balsam, were tapped with gutters and led into cans. It was a far less complicated business than the collection of its oriental counterpart.

As a result of Hanbury's first published account of storax, he began a new correspondence with F. A. Flückiger, professor of materia medica first at Berne and later at Strasburg. The two fellow pharmacists struck up a close friendship through a seven-year correspondence by letters. When they eventually met, they planned a joint work on pharmacognosy which resulted in the publication of *Pharmacographia* shortly before Hanbury died in 1875. His major contribution in this final work was a fitting end to a lifetime during which Hanbury had published nearly eighty articles on his subject.

Hanbury's correspondent in South America, the botanist and collector Richard Spruce, spent nearly twenty years studying and collecting plants in the Amazonian jungles and in the Andes mountains, and he was most certainly of the stuff for which the role of hero and martyr was designed. But he was a reluctant hero. On the one hand he can be remembered as a formidable figure, tall and shaggy-haired with a pistol in each hand, defiantly standing his ground against the threats of rampaging Indian villagers, or quieting the paranoiac frenzy of his one-time companion Charles Nelson, who threatened to do serious damage with a pick-axe handle to any near him. On the other, he may be seen contending with the miseries of fever, threats to his life and the toll that his adventures took on what he himself described as his 'delicate health and retiring disposition'. His letters home, both to William Hooker – on whose advice he had first set out on his self-imposed exile – and to Hanbury, display a preoccupation with the state of his health almost as great as that with the objects of his study. In the circumstances, however, this was rather more justified than the usual gripes of the self-centred hypochondriac. One of the most appropriate people to have commented on Spruce's historic stature is Professor Richard Schultes from Harvard University. He has been referred to as 'the father of cultural plant science', and had himself spent the greater part of his life investigating the religious and ritual significance of plants used by the South American Indians, and studying the active ingredients of these plants. To Professor Schultes, Spruce epitomised all the qualities essential to his occupation, and stands as an example to all who followed. He wrote, 'Richard Spruce still lives, and will live to fire the hearts and shape the thoughts of many a plant explorer as yet unborn, who will tread Spruce's trail to carry forward his great, unfinished work.'

Hanbury's first contact with Spruce was in the context of a request for examples of cinchona bark – the source of quinine. After a second reminder, Spruce sent a curt reply which firstly commented on his current ill-health and secondly suggested that if Hanbury was interested in cinchona bark he should read the detailed account of it that he had already sent to William Hooker. Hanbury bridled at this apparent dismissal and replied equally curtly but, despite this irritable introduction to each other, the two kept in close contact – or at least as close as the post permitted.

It is in connection with this subject that Spruce is most remembered. Quinine, as the most effective cure for malarial fever, has a long and rambling history that requires more than a brief summing up to do it full justice, but its legendary history starts with a native South American, overcome with fever, stumbling and falling into a pool of stagnant water – which he could not avoid drinking. This incident does more than reflect Paracelsus' notion of the right remedy growing in the right place, for it so happened, according to the legend, that in the water were the macerated barks of cinchona trees. The fortunate native fell into what was effectively a pool of medicine. His auspicious deliverance was relayed to Jesuit missionaries who adopted the cinchona bark as a general remedy for fevers, and for many years the powdered bark of this tree was known as Jesuits' Powder. The Jesuits sent supplies of their powder from South America to both Spain and Rome as early as 1632, and six years later its fame was assured by the rumour that it had saved the life of the Countess of Chinchon, the wife of the Viceroy of Peru. In acknowledgement, Linnaeus in the next century named the tree's genus *Cinchona*, thereby perpetrating a small spelling mistake – more than understandable considering the amount of work he undertook.

At the time that Spruce was in South America, up to two million lives, both natives' and settlers', in the empire's lands were lost each year through malarial fever, and as many permanently damaged. The worst of the regions was India. The obvious solution, once the merits of cinchona bark were fully recognised, was to introduce cinchona trees to the regions where they were most needed. The Peruvian authorities, however, were reluctant to part with seeds or cuttings from so valuable a natural resource; as usual the matter was weighed up in terms of financial advantage and trading rights rather than in terms of the universal medical benefits of the product. Both the British and Dutch were anxious to solve the problem of malaria in India and Java respectively. The first attempts by them to cultivate the trees elsewhere were not very successful. Spruce offered to collect seeds for the British government, but initially was given little encouragement. However, soon afterwards Charles Markham, formerly a clerk at the India Office, was commissioned to collect seeds for government plantations in southern India and Ceylon. He joined Spruce and, with others in their party, they set off together on a hazardous and eventful journey which eventually led high into the Andes where they procured enough seeds (100,000 of them) and seedlings to raise a million trees on Britain's plantations. For this, and for the thousands of lives that were subsequently saved by his undaunted efforts, Spruce was eventually granted, albeit reluctantly, the pitifully small retirement pension of £100 per year, for, although variously sponsored, his work had been basically 'freelance' and he had not had

Rosemary
Rosmarinus officinalis
Oil of rosemary makes a salve for wounds, bruises and rheumatic pains but it is most popularly used today as a culinary herb

the backing of an official government post. Small though this pension was, it was enough to support him in the very different surroundings of a cottage in Yorkshire, and here in 1885 he wrote his scholarly treatise on Andean and Amazonian liverwort, *Hepaticae Amazonicae et Andinae*, as well as an account of his South American travels. For all the respect that is now granted him, the tragedy was that to his contemporaries he remained a humble, i gifted and knowledgeable, gardener.

One hundred pounds a year was also the sum that the Horticultural Society paid Robert Fortune to collect for them in China ornamental or economically useful seeds and plants not already cultivated in Britain. Robert Fortune's career had humbler beginnings than those of the other plant hunters, but his achievement, swashbuckling escapades and ever-itchy feet took him further along the corridors of fame.

He began as a nurseryman's apprentice in Scotland, then moved on to the Botanic Garden in Edinburgh, and from there to London where he was given a post putting him in charge of the indoor plants at the Horticultural Society's gardens, then in Chiswick. From 1843 to 1846 he travelled in China, fought with robbers, faced pirates, disguised himself as a Chinaman, discussed philosophy with Buddhist monks and returned with as fine a collection of plants for the Horticultural Society as they could have hoped for. For two years he was curator of the Chelsea Physic Garden, but was soon off again on another expedition to China.

One of his expeditions was on behalf of the East India Company, to collect tea seeds for the government plantations in the Himalayas, although many of their plans were curtailed by the intervention of the first Indian Mutiny in 1857 and the Company itself was dissolved, nearly twenty years later, in 1874. Fortune found other employers and set off on his fourth expedition to China on behalf of the patents office in Washington, DC for their experimental station in Greenville, and returned with more than 2,000 seedlings to be greeted by the first rumblings of the American Civil War. He was always running into trouble but, being from hardy Scottish stock, he apparently thrived on it. In 1852, he presented the Pharmaceutical Society's museum with bundles of twisted leaves of 'fancy tea' – an appropriate souvenir of his Chinese travels – but on his first return in 1846 he had presented the museum with something quite different in a letter to the Society:

Tea
Camellia sinensis
Our 'common brew' is made from the leaves of a species of camellia

Aug. 25th 1846

Sir,

I beg to send you, on the recommendation of Dr Lindley [in charge of the Horticultural Society], a piece of the true ginsing *Kow-lee gin-sing* of the Chinese which I procured during my travels in China. You are doubtless aware that a kind of ginsing is exported from America to China. This is not considered by the Chinese nearly so good as their own, nor does it command such a high price on the market.

The 'Kow-Lee' or Corean ginsing is of very great value, & is considered a sort of universal cure for all diseases. Its production and sale [is] a government monopoly.

I trust you may consider the specimen sent as of interest to the Museum of The Pharmaceutical Society.

R. Fortune

Whether our medical interests are strictly orthodox or tend to the alternative, all of us must have heard at some time or another of the 'wonderful properties' of the all-powerful panacea ginseng, which is often spoken of with almost religious esteem. Indeed its generic name, *Panax*, means panacea. Perhaps the fact that its roots, rather like the mandrake, resemble the human form is contributory to this, but it would be more than philistine to dismiss it as a placebo to the millions of Chinese that think otherwise. Its properties are said to remedy practically every ailment under the sun, and in particular feverish and inflammatory illnesses, haemorrhage and blood diseases. It is also believed to be of special value to women in easing all the complaints that they are heir to – from normalising menstruation to easing childbirth – and to both sexes it is recommended as an aphrodisiac.

In England prior to the efforts of Spruce and Markham, cinchona bark – as an increasingly scarce resource and very much in demand in the overseas colonies – was obviously a worthwhile investment. The pharmacists by this time knew what it was they were looking for, as Pelletier and Caventou in France had isolated quinine from it, even though the cause of malaria, the mosquito, had not yet been identified. This came in 1902 with the investigations of Patrick Manson, founder of the London School of Tropical Medicine, and his fellow researcher Ronald Ross, formerly a doctor in the Indian Army. Luke Howard, who had been a partner at Plough Court with William Allen, set up his own chemical manufacturing business and by the 1830s was already a supplier of quinine.

As the raw materials became scarcer due to the Peruvian monopoly and inefficient replanting to meet demands, concerted efforts were being made in the trade to discover those species of cinchona bark that yielded the greatest amount of quinine. None was more active in this than Luke Howard's son, John Elliot Howard, who took over his father's business. His cinchona collection became the finest, and by far the most complete, of his day, and he himself became known as the world's most eminent quinologist – a somewhat obscure citation now, but an honour then. An illustration of the high esteem in which he was held was published after the new Indian plantations had been established in an 1867 edition of the *Chemical News* which contained an article on the exhibits of the then current Paris Exhibition. It was sent 'from our special correspondent', who began:

Fatigued with wandering from case to case . . . for owing to the perhaps inevitable distance between them, your correspondent at times has had to walk miles . . . it was a relief to come at last to a case where attempts at comparison would have been useless. I allude to the, in many respects, unrivalled display of Messrs. Howards and Sons, of Stratford. Their name has for many years held an enviable position with regard to the purity and beauty of their chemicals, and the contents of their case fully sustain their old reputation. In the English catalogue they are described thus: '48 Howards and Sons, Stratford, near London, salts of quinine and other chemicals.'

Among the many remedial agents which organic chemistry has afforded us, quinine occupies the first place, chloroform the second. Without quinine, large tracts, indeed whole countries, would be simply uninhabitable for Europeans. To the backwoodsman a supply of quinine is as important as gunpowder. The 'quinine famine' in the Mauritius demonstrated to thousands how small a thing even gold itself might become in comparison with the life-saving salt . . .

. . . The Cinchona plantations in India are now so flourishing that there need be no apprehension of the supply of quinine ever failing, and if the discovery of artificial quinine should ever now be made, it would have to depend upon its value for its cheapness . . .

. . . Messrs. Howards show an unrivalled collection of barks, including several from the new Indian plantations, and a specimen grown in England by Mr J. E. Howard . . .

John Howard's collection, including exhibits from this and the Great Exhibition of 1851, comprised hundreds of specimens, many from contemporary sources but some, and historically the most valuable, were from Ruíz and Pavon, two Spanish botanists who were among the first to determine the medicinal value of different species of bark in the 1770s. Some of the Howard and Son specimens went to the Pharmaceutical Society in his lifetime, some to the Royal College of Physicians; all, including his own personal collection, eventually found their way to the Pharmaceutical Society's museum. Needless to say, John Elliot Howard was also a friend of Hanbury's – he seemed to know everyone, or rather, in a newly developing profession, everyone knew each other.

Peruvian Bark
Cinchona officinalis
One of the many species collected by John Elliot Howard and the source of
quinine

Apart from its inestimable worth as a cure for malaria, another use was found for quinine. In the first days of the British Raj in India, they took their quinine with lime juice and a little gin to mask its bitter taste, found they liked it, and so invented a well-known tipple – gin and tonic. It was a perfect partnership. The quinine-based Indian tonic water kept the malaria at bay, and the gin the doldrums.

In 1872, Angelo Mariani, a young Corsican chemist, published in a Parisian journal a small article entitled '*Coca du Perou*', which he later followed up with two volumes – the first in 1878, the second ten years later – on the history and uses of coca leaves. He had more than a passing interest in the subject – and with good reason, for coca made him a very rich man indeed. He built conservatories at Neuilly on the Seine, where he grew thousands of coca plants for experimental purposes and began the manufacture of his greatest success, Mariani's Coca Wine. It became, not unsurprisingly, extremely popular, not only with Parisian high society but also with European royalty and even the Pope himself, who awarded its manufacturer a medal of appreciation.

Meanwhile, in Atlanta, Georgia, a pharmacist, Dr John Pemberton, was experimenting not only with coca leaves but a newly investigated fruit from West Africa, the kola nut, which had been given the generic name *Cola*. In 1886 Pemberton's new recipe went on sale in a downtown pharmacy, Jacob's, where it sold for five cents a glass from a soda fountain. It was called Coca-Cola. The name had been dreamt up by Pemberton's partner, Frank Robinson, who thought that 'the two Cs would look well in advertising'. Pemberton died two years after his great invention, and the business was bought by Asa Candler for a couple of thousand dollars – a small investment for his future millions. Ten years after its soda-fountain success, Candler was able to announce proudly: 'Coca-Cola is now drunk in every state and territory in the United States.'

Whether or not Pemberton was inspired by Mariani's innovation is a matter for conjecture, but the introduction of the kola nut is an historic one. Dr W. F. Daniell, an army medical officer and surgeon, was posted to the Gold Coast in 1850, where he found that the troops in the coastal garrison at Accra had adopted the native remedy for the frequent bouts of diarrhoea from which they suffered. This was a decoction of the fresh kola seeds, also known as bissy or gooroo nuts. He discovered that these kola seeds or nuts were, rather as the South American Indians had used coca leaves, also used as tokens of friendship, and considered a suitable offering for a prospective bridegroom to make to his future father-in-law. They were taken, like coca, as a stimulant and to combat fatigue. In the 1860s, after he had been posted to Jamaica, Daniell himself suffered a severe attack of diarrhoea and used as treatment the same kola nuts, for their trees were indigenous to the West Indies as well as West Africa. He found that he could not sleep; neither on the first night after the treatment nor the next. He put two and two together, also remembering a note made on kola nuts by an African voyager a couple of hundred years before – that taken in the evening they hindered sleep – and came up with the answer. It was only a guess at this stage but the evidence suggested to him that in the kola nut there was very likely to be 'some elementary principle analogous to caffeine'.

He was absolutely right, and subsequent analysis showed that, weight for weight, on average, kola nuts contained twice as much caffeine as the coffee bean. As an honorary member of the Pharmaceutical Society, Daniell naturally presented his findings to them, and of course donated several examples of kola nuts to their museum. On his return to Great Britain, he wrote an article for the *Pharmaceutical Journal*, entitled 'On the Kola Nut of West Tropical Africa (the Guru-nut of Soudan)', which he saw published three months before he died in June 1865.

Coca was banned from Coca-Cola in 1902 but before it shamefacedly fell into disrepute it had its honourable day. It was not just used for refreshing drinks, feats of endurance and high-spirited parties. In 1884, it became the first local anaesthetic to be used in surgery – and the only one for nearly twenty years, before it was gradually replaced by substitutes. This was not due to its inefficiency but to the realisation, when it was used to counteract the effects of morphine addiction, that it too – though it did not produce such alarming physical symptoms – was addictive. A thief was set to catch a thief and these two fugitives have been pursued ever since.

Bolivian Coca
One of the thousands of plants grown to further the success of Mariani's coca wine

The first anaesthetics had come into use in the 1840s. Until then, the patient had had to rely on the skill, and mostly the speed, of the surgeon. The use in the Middle Ages of a sponge soaked in henbane, opium and mandrake, or the use of alcohol, cannot be discounted, but ether and chloroform were the first truly effective means of alleviating the sufferings of surgery. These and other advances in the medical and affiliated sciences which were concurrent with the first decades of organised pharmacy each played a part in the shaping of its future.

Ether, its effects first noted by Michael Faraday in 1815, was initially used in surgery in 1842 and chloroform, as a preferable aid to childbirth, was introduced into medical practice by a professor of midwifery, James Simpson, in 1847. At first, the use of these anaesthetics was frowned on. The clergy felt that God was being robbed of cries for help, but such objections were firmly over-ruled in 1853 by Her Pregnant Majesty's imperious statement: 'We are having this baby, and we are having chloroform.' In the same year, the hypodermic syringe was invented and put to use two years later in 1855 to inject morphine as an anaesthetic.

Also in the 1840s, a vital clue to one of the causes of the hazards and miseries of hospital treatment was acted upon and at the same time an invention was developed which dispelled many of the mysteries of disease. In 1847, the Hungarian doctor Ignaz Semmelweiss noted the higher frequency of puerperal fever and death among newly confined mothers that were visited by doctors who had come straight to them from the dissecting room, these still being the days of unwashed hands and blood-stained frockcoats. In May of that year, he put a notice outside his maternity hospital in Vienna ordering doctors and students to wash their hands in chlorinated water before examining his patients. Following this, the death rate among his patients was reduced by 90 per cent, although he was subsequently drummed out of Vienna and home to Hungary by those who disliked his interference in their hygiene habits. Fortunately, within twenty years, a professor of surgery in Glasgow, Joseph Lister, introduced the practice of applying phenol (carbolic acid) to wounds, dressings, instruments and surgeons' hands, after reading the research of Pasteur, who had shown that disease and infection were air-borne invaders. Pasteur had been able to zoom in on micro-organisms, and so prepare for their defeat, with a microscope, which was the invention that by its development also allowed for the first identification of the invisible anatomy of a crude drug. Although Robert Hooke had first seen plant cells through a microscope in 1665, Schleiden in 1847, by having been able to differentiate between species of sarsaparilla, is recognised as having founded the microscopical study of drugs and species of plants of all kinds. As the microscope had highlighted the nature of disease, now it could define the structure of its cure.

In their newly uncovered guise, crude drugs could be more accurately identified and in the latter part of the nineteenth century, with the development of new extraction processes for alkaloids, new drugs could be isolated, old drugs studied and clues to the whereabouts of other useful species presented themselves. Cocaine was first isolated in 1860, physostigmine from the calabar bean four years later. In the 1870s, *Strophanthus*, used in arrow poisons, was investigated, resulting in the isolation of k-strophanthin and g-strophanthin or ouabain, and in 1875 pilocarpine, now used in ophthalmic medicine for its effect of contracting the pupil, was isolated from jaborandi leaf. In 1887, the Japanese isolated ephedrine from ephedra, known in China for at least 5,000 years as *Ma-huang*, which had the effect of increasing blood pressure, relieving fevers and coughs and clearing the bronchial passages. Regular habits die hard and in 1877 the purgative effects of cascara, a species of Buckthorn's bark, were introduced into medicine to join the old faithfuls castor oil, senna, Chinese rhubarb and the aloes.

Although there are in the region of 200 species of aloes, three of them became known and were highly regarded for being efficient purges. The first of these, Socotrine or Zanzibar aloes, was brought to the attention of Alexander the Great in 325 BC by his tutor Aristotle. They grew on the island of Socotra, east of the Horn of Africa, and, acting on Aristotle's suggestion, Alexander sent investigators there to find out how the drug from them was produced. All aloes have the characteristic thick fleshy leaves of the succulent, which in their case are edged with spines. When cut, from the leaves slowly drains a bitter juice which, when dried, becomes hard and brittle. Cape aloes are native to South Africa and were apparently known to the Hottentots for centuries before the first Europeans landed there. The Barbados or Curaçao aloe, still commonly referred to as aloe vera (now *Aloe barbadensis*), actually originated in the Mediterranean regions, but was taken to the West Indies in the late 1600s and later cultivated by the Dutch on the islands of Curaçao, Aruba and Bonaire at the

Socotrine Aloe
Aloe succotrina
Brought to the attention of Alexander the Great by his tutor Aristotle

beginning of the 1800s. The fresh juice of this species was an old remedy for mild skin disorders such as sunburn, minor burns, scratches or cuts, insect bites and other irritations. Nowadays, cosmetic manufacturers vow that it is one of the newly discovered 'botanical wonders', and we see it pictured and proclaimed on the packaging of shampoos, cleansing lotions, face creams and moisturisers. However, before it became so glamorous, in the nineteenth century it was still primarily used as a purge or an ornamental plant, and nowhere was it or any other species better displayed than in the splendid collection of succulents that Daniel Hanbury's brother, Thomas, cultivated in the garden of his beautiful villa, La Mortola, near Ventimiglia on the Italian riviera.

Everything in the garden at Kew was growing too, and much of the success of its exotic collections was due to an invention which had been explained by its originator to William Hooker five years before he became director of the garden. The inventor was Nathaniel Ward, and he wrote to Hooker in 1836:

My Dear Sir

I have lately heard that you wish for some information respecting my new method of growing plants without open exposure to air . . .

. . . The science of Botany, in consequence of the perusal of the works of the immortal Linnaeus, had occupied me from my youth up, and the earliest object of my ambition was to possess an old wall, covered with ferns and mosses. Compelled by circumstances to live surrounded by, and enveloped in, the smoke of numerous manufactories, all my endeavours to keep my favourites alive proved sooner or later unavailing. I was led, however, to reflect a little more deeply upon the subject, in consequence of a simple incident, which occurred about seven or eight years ago. I had buried the chrysalis of a Sphinx in some moist mould, which was contained in a wide-mouthed glass bottle, covered with a lid. In watching the bottle from day to day, I observed that the moisture, which during the heat of the day arose from the mould, condensed on the internal surface of the glass, and returned from whence it came, thus keeping the mould always equally moist. About a week prior to the final change of the insect, a seedling Fern and Grass made their appearance upon the surface of the mould . . .

He described how this had led him to construct a glass box which would enable plants and seedlings to be transported, after collection, to their destination, and he continued:

You ask how the tropical Orchideae may be best conveyed: – most certainly in the glazed cases: I believe, that, thus secured, ninety-five out of every hundred may be imported in a vigorous state from any part of the world, provided the voyage does not exceed eight or ten months in duration. In all instances, the plants require no attention during the voyage; the sole care requisite being to keep them in the light.

The Wardian Case, as it became known, was used by Kew and for Robert Fortune's tea plants. It revolutionised plant collection and had it come earlier it might have averted the famous mutiny on the *Bounty*, which resulted from the indignation of the crew at having their water rations squandered on a collection of breadfruit plants being taken from Tahiti to feed the slaves in the West Indies.

In 1858, after thirty years of parliamentary discussion, the Medical Act was passed which established new standards of education for those in the medical profession. The Medical Council was formed and, under their direction and with the assistance of the Pharmaceutical Society, in 1864 the *First British Pharmacopoeia* was published. New standards of drugs and formulae were laid down with all the benefits that the scientific revolution at that stage afforded. Change was evident in all areas of pharmaceutical manufacturers' factory floors, across the counters of retail pharmacies and on the face of their shop fronts, and by this time capsules and tablets patented in the 1840s had replaced the old-style pills and lozenges.

The name Jesse Boot has the ring of a Wild West pioneer, but he was born in Nottingham and pioneered changes in the retail of pharmaceuticals which exemplify those that took the trade from the nineteenth to the twentieth century. His beginnings were traditional, his aims and achievements modern. He began his career at the age of thirteen, helping his widowed mother in the herbalist shop she ran in Goosegate, Nottingham. In his early twenties he went into partnership with her and opened up another establishment in the same town. The fact of his success needs no mention, as every major high street in Britain bears witness to it, but it can be explained by his adoption of the simple business tactic known to all shrewd entrepreneurs, of buying in bulk, keeping prices down and undercutting rivals. For instance, he bought a ton of Epsom salts – yes, another purgative – and sold them for a penny a pound when others sold them for a penny an ounce. His rivals were put out by this and criticised him for being an unqualified chemist. This had no effect on either public opinion or his business, which went from strength to strength. The displays in his shop were new and attractive, packaging and presentation of his products were carefully considered, and he adopted the slogan 'Boots the Cash Chemist', which meant that instead of customers running up large accounts, sometimes difficult to settle, they paid on the nail for what they purchased, and at his prices were glad to do so. After he married in his thirties, his equally enterprising wife suggested that his merchandise should also include cosmetics, perfumes and 'toilet requisites', thereby making his business more general and more popular still. By 1900, Boots was well on the way to having 200 branches, which opened their doors to the twentieth century.

6

New Growth

Medical and pharmaceutical achievements in the twentieth century would fill a book, let alone a section of one. However, it is not the purpose of this chapter to document their historic order or to put dates to them, but rather to show them in perspective to the present.

It is not easy to obtain a true perspective. We may get a wonderfully clear view of our planet from the starry vantage point of a satellite – but then we lose sight of ourselves. Down on the ground, we see only those things immediately around us. What is needed – and what is technically impossible – is to see both views at once and we have only our imaginations to conjure the scene. Nevertheless, it takes but a small amount of this to see that what we are faced with is an imbalanced world.

If the nineteenth century was an age of invention and innovation, the staggering amount of changes that the next brought must make the twentieth the fastest-moving century that our species has known so far. These changes are usually described as advances. But were they all?

Circumnavigating the world in 108 minutes was truly an advance in speed. Landing on the moon was truly an advance in technology. Our being able to see and hear events taking place thousands of miles away has been truly an advance in communications and an expansion of horizons. The discovery of vitamins, new vaccines, antibiotics and the refinement of surgical skills that have allowed for organ transplants are all truly medical advances. A hundred or more proclaimed breakthroughs a year give the impression of one almighty and universal surge forward of humankind with a deafening yell of triumph, but it is a false impression. We face an uncertain future from the standpoint of a precarious present.

On a social level the picture is somewhat different. Many things can and have been changed, but human behaviour remains the same. We would like to think, for example, that were public executions to be reintroduced in this country we would not attend them. Haven't all of us watched unflinchingly a hundred gruesome scenes on television, enacted or real? Real-life tragedies shown on our screens take on the same quality of unreality: documentary becomes drama. Sometimes a particular point will strike home – cheque books will be flourished and charities funded – but it will be forgotten the next day. It is not that we all have hearts of stone, but that in an age of information technology we are pathetically ill-informed about the things that really matter or how we can help each other and our descendants, let alone ourselves.

Starving people having their suppers sung for them by well-meaning pop stars is a very worthwhile gesture, but it is not an advance and even goes to demonstrate with ghastly clarity the chasm between the haves and the have nots. Locking law breakers away simply slams the door on problems that could be solved in other ways. Although their treatment is improved and refined, increases in heart diseases and cancer cases do not demonstrate advances in the layman's medical education or the application of preventitive measures by which many of these problems could be averted. From the point of view of general health, what the majority of us could do with, as Hippocrates advocated, is a spell in the mountains, fresh air and a simple diet, but it's a busy world and as humdrum as ever and, although we may fly across the skies in planes, most of us will never reach even the nursery slopes of those mountainsides.

While one family on one side of the world may wage war against overweight, what is left of another, on the other side of it, may never gain a single ounce between its members – though they may long to. The idea of a publication entitled *How to Stop Starving* or *Eat and Live Longer* is ludicrous – but then so is the situation. On one hand feast, on the other famine. Both bring disease. Modern medical treatment and pharmaceuticals will help both heart patient and famine victim but can do little to change the environmental and social problems that cause them.

What is clear is that there is a marked difference between scientific and social advance and it has become a case of the human species running before it is fully equipped to walk. While scientists race ahead, hell for leather, they leave the majority of us behind, struggling to keep up, not only with the understanding of their achievements but with their consequences which the scientists themselves are not necessarily able to predict.

With the best will in the world, scientists have pursued the fascinating leads of their discoveries because they are able to do so and because human nature is inquisitive. We all know what happened to the proverbially curious cat. When Anton van Leeuwenhoek watched under a microscope those 'little animals moving about in a most delightful manner', he could not have conceived of the threat of 'germ warfare'. When Pierre and Marie Curie watched their discovery, the 'Shining Element' radium, glowingly self-destruct in the dark; when Einstein equated what they had seen with matter converting into energy; when Ernest Rutherford called ions 'jolly little beggars' or announced that 'the atom has been split'; when Otto Hahn first discovered atomic fission – could any of them have known how their research and strivings in the name of science would result in the atomic horror of Hiroshima? Otto Hahn must have understood to an extent the implications of his experiments but he did not envisage what actually occurred and broke down with guilt and grief when he heard that the atomic bomb had been dropped. Of little comfort to him was the Nobel Prize he was later awarded.

Similarly, although it may seem unfair to cite a failure in a field that has achieved so much for the good, the tragedy of thalidomide was an unfortunate oversight in pharmaceutical trials. This mild sedative appeared to have no ill-effects on laboratory animals or human guinea pigs and as all tests proved reassuring there seemed no reason to suppose that disastrous deformities would result in their offspring. No one deliberately intended that by prescribing Valium to counteract the pressures from the quickened pace of modern living new problems of dependency would arise. If we look to another area of medicine, can anyone say yet with absolute certainty that the advent of the phenomena of sperm banks and test-tube babies will not see the dawn of another disaster? Even if we can be assured of the results on one hand, and can be convinced that the benefits to childless couples are well worth the efforts made in this field or can be satisfied that the forebodings of cloning are nothing more than scaremongerings and sensationalism, doesn't this scientific advance make a bizarre contrast to the social problem of overpopulation?

Not only do we see a jarring contrast between what has been achieved scientifically and technically, and what has been achieved in terms of social improvement, but we are also faced with the uncertainty of how ultimately the former will affect the latter. It would be a horrible irony if the very things designed to improve the world were in the end responsible for ruining it.

Therefore it is vital to the future of our species that social and other scientists should work together with the aim of achieving a balance between what is scientifically and technically possible and what is socially desirable. At the same time, we must all guard against the mistake of relinquishing or dismissing as redundant anything that has in the past been of value to us. For instance, if synthetic foods came to monopolise the world market it would be sensible to preserve some acres of agricultural land and keep the seeds of traditional food crops germinating. Currently it is important that care should be taken to cultivate for conservation some members of each species of indigenous plants.

If all the man-made medicines in the world, or the means to make them, were somehow destroyed – and we dare not think how – yet plants and some of us remained, medicines would still be made, independent of our manufacture. While plants are allowed to flourish we are guaranteed the air we breathe, shelter, clothing, food and medicine. They are all we need in order to survive and yet they are trampled underfoot, dismissed, torn up and pulled down. Ecologists and conservationists do their best but until they are given full co-operation it will not be enough.

Edward Morrell Holmes, who became curator of the Pharmaceutical Society's museum in 1872, devoted himself for the next fifty years to studying, cataloguing, lecturing and writing on the specimens of crude drugs and their derivatives in his care. When he retired at the age of seventy-nine this materia medica museum collection was already being seen by some members of the Pharmaceutical Society as a curiosity rather than a useful aid to the School of Pharmacy's curriculum. In the nineteenth century it was useful for a student of pharmacy to be able to distinguish, by sensory comparison, between raw materials. The worth of some quinine barks could be told simply by looking at them. Crumbling, sniffing and squinting were all valid means of examination. But with the increase in the use of synthetic chemicals and the decline in the use of vegetable drugs it came to be felt that examining these raw materials and learning something of their history and origins was no longer entirely necessary.

Chemical analysis and microscopical study distanced the student further from the crude drug. When the degree of Bachelor of Pharmacy was introduced by the University of London in 1924, botany and chemistry became part of the syllabus and when later the School of Pharmacy introduced the newly defined subject, pharmaceutical chemistry, which included the chemistry and analysis of inorganic and organic substances used in medicine, the chemistry and evaluation of drugs was no longer part of pharmacognosy's scope. It became a dismembered subject. Some of the details that Daniel Hanbury would have considered important to the knowledge of a crude drug were no longer considered salient. He had driven himself nearly mad with trying to find out where, exactly, Peru balsam originated – now it scarcely mattered.

E. M. Holmes
Curator of the Pharmaceutical Society's Museum for fifty years

When Dr T. Wallis, like his predecessor a stickler for facts, spotted a mistake in the details of how honey bees pluck wax scales from their sternums, printed in the fifth edition of his *Textbook on Pharmacognosy*, he was told that it was scarcely a point of any significance.

Although Dr T. Wallis was greatly respected by his colleagues and pharmacy students, his critics may well have been right in this particular matter, but when details are lost through being considered of no importance, or those who find them fascinating are not particularly encouraged in their pursuit, something of the whole quality of a subject is lost.

As a result of the disruption to trading caused by the Second World War and of the bombing of the London Docks, there was a great reduction in the importation of crude drugs. Besides this, the war had (as wars always do) led to rapid developments in the medical sciences. Unavailability of crude drugs and new processes of preparing and synthesising drugs saw a further decline in the traditional study of the raw materials. By the 1950s it had already been said that pharmacognosy no longer had any place in the curriculum of pharmacy. Some were not only eager to retain pharmacognosy as a subject but suggested that the syllabus should be expanded to incorporate modern means of gaining 'a knowledge of drugs'. It was retained but remained reduced in content.

However, just at the time when pharmacognosy was being regarded in some academic circles as a thing of the past, the potentiality of plants as sources of medicinal agents was being considered with renewed interest by the governments and universities of developing countries and various international organisations such as the World Health Organisation and UNESCO. It made economic and social sense to make the best use of what could be home grown, whether it was food or medicine. This was not to condemn the effectiveness of modern drugs, but it drew attention to the need to keep old ones in reserve for study, not to forget them and not to be so certain that the uses of those drugs over and above the ones still retained in pharmacy were redundant.

Already in the 1920s, Joseph Rock had been commissioned by the United States Department of Agriculture to investigate the true sources of the legendary chaulmoogra oil, effective in treating leprosy and of which there were inadequate supplies to meet the rising demands. His adventures were on a par with those of his nineteenth-century predecessors. Setting off from Hawaii, he sailed to Singapore, travelled 1,000 miles overland to Bangkok and a further 400 miles on a wild goose chase before turning tail and undergoing a hazardous ten-day trip along rapids. His search took him across the mountains by bullock cart to Burma after which, in traditional plant-hunter style, he faced the usual type of perils – bandits, fever, setbacks and near-escapes. He witnessed the uproar of a village threatened by a man-eating tiger which killed two of the inhabitants before it was slain and slung across two poles by its triumphant trappers – who returned with it only to find that their homes had been trampled underfoot by rampaging elephants. Rock finally reported back with his finds: seeds from two species of *Hydnocarpus* and from a species of the closely related *Taraktogenus*, these three specific trees being the likeliest providers of the anciently used chaulmoogra oil. Although *Hydnocarpus* or chaulmoogra oil has in recent years been replaced by other remedies, the type of investigations that were undertaken in relation to it continued.

In the late 1940s, another traditional remedy, this time from India, was reinvestigated. Snakeroot was an old treatment for cases of insanity, and laboratory tests showed it to be effective in reducing blood pressure and to have a calming effect on those showing signs of extreme anxiety. In 1954, reserpine was isolated from it and used in general medicine as a tranquilliser which had the benefit of not producing the usual groggy side effects, and for cases of hypertension. Also in the 1950s, alkaloids from species of periwinkle were investigated, following a thirteenth-century lead which gave the common blue periwinkle as a cure for nose-bleeds and evidence from the seventeenth century which held it to be useful in treating chest inflammations. Subsequently, from the closely related Madagascar periwinkle, six of its about ninety alkaloids proved active in destroying white blood cells and one of them, Vincristine (leurocristine), came to be used in cases of childhood leukaemia. This plant became a prime example among many which were being newly cited as potentially useful in cancer therapy. In the 1970s a patient in a London hospital was in danger of dying from the wound left by a kidney operation. An inspired doctor, who happened to know that an old African remedy for deep cuts that were reluctant to heal was a poultice of pawpaw, sent out for some of this fruit. It was brought, dissected and applied to the wound. After three days the patient was off the danger list, on the mend and in the headlines.

In most cases, these and other remedies were age-old, if not fully exploited, but they were popularly reported as 'New Botanic Wonders'. This type of publicity coincided with a general back-to-nature movement which reached a zenith in the 1960s and did not actually reflect their true worth. Traditional medicine was referred to as 'folk medicine' and it took on 'folksy' connotations, making it all seem a little bit trendy. Of course, the researchers involved in these investigations were serious scientists and anything but sensationalists, but sensational publicity has a way of defeating its own purpose. When absolutely genuine and well-researched discoveries are proclaimed as 'Amazing Breakthroughs', 'Plant Magic' or 'Wonder Cures', they lose something of their impetus – it becomes journalism and is treated with the same 'We've heard it all before' attitude by the layman.

The merits of medicine should be based on facts rather than left to general impressions, but two factions of popular opinion arose. Investigations were being made into traditional medicines and new ones were being searched for among species of plants related to those that had already proved useful in this context. This was not intended to be seen as advocating *only* traditional medicines or as a criticism of *all* modern ones but unfortunately an 'either/or' syndrome resulted. There were those that staunchly held on to proven present methods of treatment and those that believed in returning wholesale to the old ways. Both sides had their points but one particular point did not seem to be fully appreciated by either faction. The commonly used phrase 're-turning to old ways' gives the impression of harking back to the past, or at least to the ways of those in some dark Amazonian forest, and smacks of more than a little Western World conceit – or shortsightedness. The fact that as little as 10 per cent of the world's population are regular benefiters of Western orthodox medicine begs the question; return from what?

For many years, before the whole issue became almost a matter of fashion in the 1960s, it was the official policy of many developing countries to utilise their traditional medicines. On the home front, among white communities, herbalism was not a new thing and had hundreds of long-standing supporters. Hindu, Chinese, West Indian and African communities, living alongside our own, each had their own traditional medicines and medical practices. Of the 2,000-odd drugs used by the Hindus in their Ayurvedic medicine, 75 per cent are directly plant-based and can be bought from shops within their communities. Chinatown in the heart of London's West End still has shops selling traditional remedies, and they are more than ethnic curiosities to be peeped at – those seeing them as such would be met with an icy stare. It's true that some Chinese medicines are a little difficult for westerners to swallow, particularly items such as various beetles, bear's galls and bat's excreta, not to mention magpie droppings, cicadas, earthworms, burnt human hair and urinary deposits, but although they are different from our medicines they exist alongside them and are not things of the past.

Living proof that the so-called 'old ways' are still very much part of the present can be found at a shop called Baldwins in London's Elephant and Castle. There are a great many attractive things about this shop. There is the pleasant herbal smell, the bottles of flower oils, the cheery atmosphere and, whatever the weather, a refreshing glass of sarsaparilla can be bought across the counter. The best thing is that, although its fittings do lend an air of old-world charm, the shop does not give a sense of being an old-world curiosity. It is a thriving business catering for a grateful community, just as it has done for a hundred years. There is nothing of the 'fad' about it. There are no affectations, no pretty prepacked bottles of essential oils or lace-edged pot-pourri parcels selling at ridiculous prices. If you want to buy an essential oil, and most are supplied, it's measured out into a no-nonsense phial and labelled for you – the only possible criticism here being that after much use the ink can smear and then you have to remember what fragrance it is you're wearing. If you want pot-pourri, it's ladled into a simple paper bag. Many of Baldwins' customers nowadays are West Indians who are able to buy their familiar remedies there, or the ingredients to mix them, and it's nice to see these things being requested and dispensed as matter of factly as if they were everyday commodities – which of course they are in this shop.

Sarsaparilla
Smilax spp.
Popularly used as a blood purifier and tonic

147

Three miles away from Baldwins, the present headquarters of the Pharmaceutical Society stands. It gazes rather grandly across the Thames to Westminster and down on to the grounds of Lambeth Palace where, at the gate, is the Church of St Mary Lambeth, now converted into the Museum of Gardening History. The Tradescants, father and son, are buried in its churchyard and also the bones of Bligh of the *Bounty* fame.

When the Pharmaceutical Society first decided in 1967 to move from Bloomsbury Square to these new headquarters, the building plans did not provide a space for the Society's materia medica museum collection. Although it was recognised as being one of the largest and most prestigious collections of crude drugs in the world and an invaluable source of authentic material for research, it had already been decided that a space should be found for it elsewhere. The question was: where? At first Chelsea College of Science and Technology was considered but, after a provisional agreement, Chelsea found that it did not have sufficient space. Bradford University at this time did have the space and in 1968 the collection was housed in its School of Pharmacy. It remained there for fifteen years, only to be moved on again in 1983. By this time the collection was rather more than the few brown paper parcels it began with. There were by now in the region of 20,000 specimens, most of them stored in heavy metal cabinets, and the whole lot weighed about twelve and a half tons. Had Holmes been alive to see his precious collection, which he had lovingly curated for half a century, first sent packing from its first home to way up North, only to be later rejected and sent elsewhere, it would certainly have made him sad. But he would as certainly have been cheered to know where it eventually went. It went to Kew.

If it had to leave the Pharmaceutical Society at all, it could hardly have gone to a more suitable place. The setting was perfect – one great and beautiful garden. All the kindred associations were there. And what had gone into the making of Kew and the Society's museum collection was more than kindred – it was the same spirit. Kew Gardens is there not only to give the pleasure of its vistas, its lake and all its thousands of plants, exotic and brilliantly coloured or fragile and intricately detailed, but to ensure that all the benefits that plants provide us with may be studied and developed. In return, Kew stores their seeds and protects them. They are, after all, our only truly reliable safeguards. It is a comforting thought that, in an age that dashes on, leaving in its wake a litter of lost causes, Kew treads steadily in a positive direction.

After the Pharmaceutical Society's museum collection was moved to Kew in 1983, it was arranged into taxonomic order, tidied up and locked away in one huge room of the wood museum prior to being incorporated with the Gardens' own collections in the new museum, then being built. Few came to refer to it for study. It went into safe and honourable retirement; in a sense it resembled a dead collection. But there is dead and there is dormant.

One of the specimens in the collection was a jar of ginkgo seeds from Japan, donated by a firm of chemists, Thomas Christy's, in 1878. The ginkgo, having evolved in the region of 25,000,000 years ago, is a resilient tree; its fan-shaped leaf is one of Kew's symbols. Out of interest, two or three of the seeds were taken to see if they were still viable. They were popped in a couple of pots, put away and more or less forgotten about. Then one of them started growing. This living tree, which at the time of writing is about to open its leaves to a fourth year's growth, expresses more than any treatise can the collection's vitality, its potential and the lessons still to be learned from it.

Bibliography

Books

Dannie Abse, *Medicine on Trial*, Aldus Books, 1967

Lynn Barber, *The Heyday of Natural History*, Jonathan Cape, 1980

Black's Medical Dictionary, A. & C. Black, 1981 (33rd edition)

William Breckon, *The Drug Makers*, Methuen, 1972

Butterworths' Medical Dictionary, Butterworths, 1980 (2nd edition)

Nigel Calder, *Timescale*, The Hogarth Press, 1984

Carlos Castaneda, *Teachings of Don Juan: Yaqui Way of Knowledge*, Penguin, 1970

——, *Separate Reality: Further Conversations with Don Juan*, Penguin, 1973

——, *Journey to Ixtlan: Lessons of Don Juan*, Penguin, 1975

Classification of the Animal Kingdom, Reader's Digest, 1972

Vernon Coleman, *The Story of Medicine*, Robert Hale, 1985

Concise Medical Dictionary, Oxford Medical Publications, 1985 (2nd edition)

M. C. Cook, *A Plain and Easy Account of British Funghi*, 1862

I. W. Cornwall, *The World of Ancient Man*, J. M. Dent & Sons, 1964

Nicholas Culpeper, *Culpeper's Complete Herbal*, P. W. Foulsham & Co.

Charles Darwin, *On the Origin of Species*, Murray, 1859

Erasmus Darwin, *Zoonomia; or the Laws of Organic Life*, 1794–6

Stephen Jay Gould, *Ever Since Darwin*, Penguin, 1977

Howard W. Haggard, *Devils, Drugs and Doctors*, Heinemann, 1929

F. E. Halliday, *A Concise History of England*, Thames & Hudson, 1986

Paul Hastings, *Medicine: An International History*, Ernest Benn, 1974

Anthony J. Huxley, *Green Inheritance: World Wildlife Fund Book of Plants*, Collins, 1984

Edward Hyams, *Plants in the Service of Man*, J. M. Dent & Sons, 1971

Brian Inglis, *Natural Medicine*, Collins, 1979

Betty Jackson, 'From Papyri to Pharmacopoeia', an offprint from *The Evolution of Pharmacy in Britain*, Pitman Medical Publishing Co.

Ronald King, *Royal Kew*, Constable, 1985

B. Lehane, *The Power of Plants*, John Murray, 1977

John Lust, *The Herb Book*, Bantam Books, 1986

Charles Lyte, *The Plant Hunters*, Orbis, 1983

Mark David Merlin, *On the Trail of the Ancient Opium Poppy*, London Associated University Presses, 1984

Colin Patterson, *Evolution*, Routledge & Kegan Paul, 1978

Penguin Medical Encyclopedia, Penguin, 1972

John M. Riddle, *Dioscorides on Pharmacy and Medicine*, University of Texas Press, 1985

Richard Evans Schultes, *Hallucinogenic Plants*, Golden Press

Professor E. J. Shellard, *A History of British Pharmacognosy 1842–1980*, 1980

Dr Henry Ernst Sigerist, *History of Medicine: Vol. 1 Primitive and Archaic Medicine*, Oxford University Press, 1951

Ralph Solecki, *Shanidar: The Humanity of Neanderthal Man*, Alfred A. Knopf, 1971

Norman Taylor, *Plant Drugs that Changed the World*, Allen & Unwin, 1965

G. E. Trease and W. C. Evans, *Pharmacognosy*, Ballière Tindall, 1983

G. E. Trease, *Pharmacy in History*, Ballière Tindall & Cox, 1964

Erik Trinkaus, *The Shanidar Neanderthals*, A. C. Press, 1983

Colin Turnbull, *Mountain People*, Ballière Tindall & Cox, 1964

E. Ashworth Underwood, Introduction to *Wellcome Historical Medical Museum Catalogue of an exhibition illustrating the medicine of aboriginal peoples in the British Commonwealth*, Oxford University Press, 1952

William Withering, *An Account of the Foxglove*, 1785

Journals

A. E. Bailey, 'Early Nineteenth-century Pharmacy', *Pharmaceutical Journal*, 3 September 1960

Professor G. B. Marini Bertolo, 'The Evolution of the Pharmacopoeias in Europe', *Pharmaceutical Journal*, 19 November 1966

David L. Cowen, 'History and Pharmacy', *Pharmaceutical Journal*, 30 January 1960

Arlette Leroi-Gourhan, 'The Flowers Found with Shanidar IV, a Neanderthal Burial in Iraq', *Science*, Vol. 190, 7 November 1975

'Museum of the Pharmaceutical Society', *Pharmaceutical Journal*, 2 February 1878

Dr R. W. D. Nickalls, 'W. F. Daniel 1817–1865 and the Discovery that Cola-nuts Contain Caffeine', *Pharmaceutical Journal*, 3 March 1986

E. J. Shellard, 'Materia Medica Museum and Herbaria', *Pharmaceutical Journal*, 18 March 1972

J. T. Slugg, 'The Pharmacy of the Bible', *Pharmaceutical Journal*, April 1872

Joyce A. Tyldesley and Paul G. Bahn, 'Use of Plants in the European Palaeolithic: A Review of the Evidence', *Quaternary Science Review*, Vol. 2, 1983

Index of Common and Botanical Names

Cannabis	*Cannabis sativa*
Cape aloes	*Aloe ferox*
Cardamom	*Elettaria cardamomum*
Cascara	*Rhamnus purshiana*
Cashew tree	*Anacardium occidentale*
Castor oil	*Ricinus communis*
Cedar	*Cedrus sp.*
Cedria	*Cedrus libani*
Chaulmoogra oil	*Hydnocarpus kurzii*
Cherry laurel	*Prunus laurocerasus*
Chillies	*Capsicum spp.*
China root	*Smilax glabra*
Chinese rhubarb	*Rheum palmatum*
Christmas rose	*Helleborus spp.*
Cinnamon	*Cinnamomum zeylanicum*
Clove	*Syzygium aromaticum*
Coca	*Erythroxylon coca*
Coca du Perou	*Erythroxylon coca*
Cocoa	*Theobroma cacao*
Coffee	*Coffea arabica & canephora*
Coltsfoot	*Tussilago farfara*
Common oak	*Quercus robur*
Cork oak	*Quercus suber*
Corn	*Zea mays*
Cornflower	*Centaurea cyanus*
Cowslip	*Primula veris*
Crocus	probably *Crocus sativus*
Croton	*Croton tiglium*
Crude storax	*Liquidambar orientalis*
Cucumber	*Cucumis sativus*
Cumin	*Cuminum cyminum*
Curacao aloe	*Aloe barbadensis*
Curare	*Chondrodendron tomentosum &* *Strychnos toxifera*
Damask rose	*Rosa centifolia*
Dandelion	*Taraxacum officinale*
Date	*Phoenix dactylifera*
Date palm	*Phoenix dactylifera*
Dock	*Rumex spp.*
Dog rose	*Rosa canina*
Dogbane	*Apocynum androsaemifolium*
Drop storax	*Liquidambar orientalis*
Drum storax	*Liquidambar orientalis*
Egyptian privet	*Lawsonia inermis*
Ergot	*Claviceps purpurea*
Fennel	*Foeniculum vulgare*
Fenugreek	*Trigonella foenum-graecum*
Fig	*Ficus carica*
Flag	*Iris sp.*
Fly agaric	*Amanita muscaria*
Four-leafed clover	*Trifolium sp.*
Foxglove	*Digitalis purpurea*
Frankincense	*Boswellia spp.*
Garden pea	*Pisum sativum*
Garlic	*Allium sativum*
Gentian	*Gentiana lutea*
Ginger	*Zingiber officinale*

Ginseng	*Panax ginseng*
Gooroo nut	*Cola acuminata*
Gorse	*Ulex europaeus*
Grape hyacinth	*Muscari sp.*
Great mullein	*Verbascum thapsus*
Great plantain	*Plantago major*
Groundsel	*Senecio vulgaris*
Guaiacum	*Guaiacum officinale*
Gum storax	*Liquidambar orientalis*
Guru-nut of Soudan	*Cola acuminata*
Hashish	*Cannabis sativa*
Hazel	*Corylus avellana*
Hellebore	*Helleborus sp.*
Hemp	*Cannabis sativa*
Henbane	*Hyoscyamus niger*
Henna	*Lawsonia inermis*
Holly	*Ilex aquifolium*
Hollyhock	*Althaea rosea*
Horehound	*Marrubium sp.*
Hound's-tongue	*Cynoglossum officinale*
Iboga	*Tabernanthe iboga*
Ipecacuanha	*Cephaelis ipecacuanha*
Jaborandi	*Pilocarpus spp.*
Jackass tree	*Trachylobium sp.*
Jalap	*Ipomoea purga*
Jesuits' powder	powdered bark of *Cinchona spp.*
Jimson weed	*Datura stramonium*
Juniper	*Juniperus communis*
Kawa-no-no-no-kawa	*Morus alba*
Kola	*Cola acuminata*
Kow-lee gin-sing	*Panax ginseng*
Lavender	*Lavandula angustifolia*
Lemon	*Citrus limon*
Levant storax	*Liquidambar orientalis*
Lilac	*Syringa vulgaris*
Lily of the valley	*Convallaria majalis*
Lime	*Tilia x vulgaris*
Linseed	*Linum usitatissimum*
Liquid storax	*Liquidambar orientalis*
Liquorice	*Glycyrrhiza glabra*
Ma-huang	*Ephedra spp.*
Mace	*Myristica fragrans*
Madagascar periwinkle	*Catharanthus roseus*
Maidenhair tree	*Ginkgo biloba*
Mallow	*Malva sylvestris*
Mandrake	*Mandragora officinarum*
Marmalade	*Citrus aurantium*
Marrow	*Cucurbita pepo*
Meadowsweet	*Filipendula ulmaria*
Melon	*Cucumis melo*
Michaelmas daisy	*Aster novi-belgii*
Mint	*Mentha spp.*
Monkshood	*Aconitum napellus*
Morning glory	*Rivea corymbosa & Ipomoea sp.,* maybe *I. tricolor*
Mulberry	*Morus nigra*
Mustard	*Brassica nigra*

Myrrh	*Commiphora molmol*
Myrrh tree of Arabia	*Commiphora molmol*
Naked ladies	*Colchicum autumnale*
Nasturtium	*Tropaeolum majus*
Neroli	*Citrus aurantium*
Nettle	*Urtica dioica*
Nutmeg	*Myristica fragrans*
Nux vomica	*Strychnos nux-vomica*
Oak	*Quercus spp.*
Oat	*Avena sativa*
Olive	*Olea europaea*
Ololiuqui	*Rivea corymbosa*
Onion	*Allium cepa*
Opium	*Papaver somniferum*
Opium poppy	*Papaver somniferum*
Orange	*Citrus sinensis*
Orchidacene	*Orchidaceae*
Papyrus	*Cyperus papyrus*
Pawpaw	*Carica papaya*
Peony	*Paeonia sp.*
Pepper	*Piper nigrum*
Periwinkle	*Vinca minor*
Peru balsam	*Myroxylon balsamum var pereirae*
Papaver setigerum	*Papaver somniferum ssp. setigerum*
Peruvian bark	*Cinchona spp.*
Peyote	*Lophophora williamsii*
Pomegranate	*Punica granatum*
Poppy	*Papaver somniferum*
Potato	*Solanum tuberosum*
Prepared storax	*Liquidambar orientalis*
Provence rose	*Rosa gallica*
Purging cassia	*Cassia fistula*
Purified storax	*Liquidambar orientalis*
Purple foxglove	*Digitalis purpurea*
Quinine	*Cinchona spp.*
Radish	*Raphanus sativus*
Raffia	*Raphia pedunculata*
Raisin	*Vitis vinifera*
Raspberry	*Rubus idaeus*
Red bean	*Sophora secundiflora*
Red maple	*Acer rubrum*
Red oak	*Quercus rubra*
Red palm oil	*Elaeis guineensis*
Reed	*Phragmites australis*
Rose	*Rosa spp.*
Rosehips	*Rosa canina & Rosa rugosa*
Rosemary	*Rosmarinus officinalis*
Rue	*Ruta graveolens*
Rum	*Saccharum officinarum*
Runner bean	*Phaseolus coccineus*
Rye	*Secale cereale*
Saffron	*Crocus sativus*
Sandalwood	*Santalum album*
Sarsaparilla	*Smilax spp.*
Sassy bark	*Erythrophleum guineense*
Sauerkraut	*Brassica oleracea*
Saxifrage	*Saxifraga sp.*

Scammony	*Convolvulus scammonia*
Senna	*Cassia senna & Cassia angustifolia*
Slippery elm	*Ulmus rubra*
Snakeroot	*Rauwolfia serpentina*
Soapwort	*Saponaria officinalis*
Socotrine aloe	*Aloe succotrina*
Solid storax	*Liquidambar orientalis*
Squirting cucumber	*Ecballium elaterium*
St Barnaby's thistle	*Centaurea solstitialis*
Storax	anciently *Styrax officinale*, recently *Liquidamber orientalis*
Styrax	*Liquidambar orientalis*
Styrax Balsam	*Liquidambar orientalis*
Styrax Calamita	*Liquidambar orientalis*
Styrax Praeparatus	*Liquidambar orientalis*
Sweet almond	*Prunus dulcis*
Sweet gum	*Liquidambar styraciflua*
Tanguin nut	*Cerbera tanghin*
Tansy	*Tanacetum vulgare*
Taraktogenus	*Hydnocarpus spp.*
Tea	*Camellia sinensis*
Thistle	*Cirsium sp.*
Tinnevelly senna	*Cassia angustifolia*
Tobacco	*Nicotiana tabacum*
Tulip tree	*Liriodendron tulipifera*
Turpentine	*Pinus spp.*
Upas tree	*Antiaris toxicaria*
Urari	see Curare
Vanilla	*Vanilla planifolia*
Vervain	*Verbena officinalis*
Vetch	*Vicia spp.*
Violet	*Viola spp.*
Virginia creeper	*Parthenocissus quinquefolia*
Virginian tobacco	*Nicotiana tabacum*
Walnut	*Juglans regia*
White birch	*Betula alba*
White cabbage	*Brassica oleracea*
White foxglove	*Digitalis lanata*
White hellebore	*Veratrum album*
White mulberry	*Morus alba*
White poplar	*Populus alba*
White willow	*Salix alba*
Willow	*Salix sp.*
Woody horsetail	*Ephedra sp.*
Wormwood	*Artemisia absinthium*
Yarrow	*Achillea millefolium*
Yellow gentian	*Gentiana lutea*
Zanzibar aloes	*Aloe perryi*
Zedoary	*Kaempferia rotunda*

Index

Page numbers in *italic* refer to the illustrations